FEEL Great

BE THE **BEST** YOU CAN BE

Published by

Humm Publishing

Part of Humm Media Limited
Union House,
20 Kentish Town Road,
London, NW1 9NX

hello@hummmedia.com
www.hummmedia.com

© Oliver Gray 2016
© Humm Media 2016

ISBN: 978-0-9934271-1-4

Printed in Great Britain by TJ International
Cover and page design: Laura Hawkins
Handwritten cover text: Chelsea Rose

FEEL
Great

BE THE **BEST** YOU CAN BE

Develop an innovative approach to mindfulness
combined with advanced, yet simple, habits
for your health, energy and happiness

OLIVER GRAY

A NOTE FROM THE AUTHOR

Coaching people to be the best they can be is my passion.

Now it's your turn. In reading this book you'll
have all the ingredients to start your journey
to becoming the best you can be.

You'll learn:

· How to create new habits in 30 days
· An innovative approach to mindfulness
· More than 100 advanced, yet simple, habits for your
health, energy and happiness

BIG THANKS

Thank you for all your great feedback, Poppy, Dad,
Lucy, Katy, Andrew, Claudia, Oana, Karin, Lizzy, Liz,
Elisabeth, Sally, Laura, Sam, Dominique, Zandra, Camilla,
Camille, Claire, Chelsea, Jill, Jane, Susi, Chris, Susie and Karen

CONTENTS

TIPS AND QUOTES

My mission with this book

I have two huge passions in my life:

1. My own health, energy and happiness.
I love to evolve continually and to work on being the best I can be, both physically and mentally. I believe our minds and bodies are the most magical gifts, so I believe we must keep them healthy, energised and happy. I am passionate about learning new ways to achieve these goals.

2. Helping others to achieve greater health, energy and happiness.
I love taking everything I learn and sharing this in a simple way to help others – and so I have written this book.

My thinking behind the book covers seven key elements. These have come together with one simple question in mind: "At this time, what are the most important components to help people achieve greater health, energy and happiness?"

They are as follows:

1. The first is to ensure I create a simple, practical book that is concise and easy to follow. I know your time is precious and you need me to cut through all the noise and explain what to do and how to do it in the simplest way possible.

2. I will start by drawing your attention to the current situation, i.e. the problem with the modern way of living and how the wrong habits are negatively affecting our health, energy and happiness.

3. I will explain why people find habit change so challenging. I will then give you a simple, practical and highly effective way of achieving the small habit changes in your life that

will deliver big results for your health, energy and happiness.

4. I will explain why mindfulness is the key habit through which to achieve great health, energy and happiness.

5. I will cover the main challenges people have with mindfulness, why they struggle so much with this habit and I will give you a simple approach to mindfulness to make it practical and achievable.

6. Once you understand how to achieve change and this simple approach to mindfulness, you will have a strong base from which to approach the rest of the book. I cover all the best habits for your health, energy and happiness in the key areas of your life.

You can then use this as your manual to make continual changes, over time. Everyone is unique, so don't feel you have to do everything in this book – just find the habits that work for you.

7. The final part of the book includes quotes and tips to inspire you to change. So when you feel your motivation levels dropping, you can read some of these to get fired up again to make change.

Everything in this book has worked for my own health, energy and happiness, but more importantly, it has helped thousands of individuals in the hundreds of organisations with which my company, EnergiseYou, has worked, since 2004.

I know this book can help you and I will be truly excited to hear about your results.

The key philosophy of this book

This is not a book to be read like a normal book.

Most people read self-help books and learn some new stuff and then start their next book and learn some more stuff.

The problem with this approach is that all you are doing is increasing your knowledge, but simply having more information and knowledge will not improve your health, energy and happiness.

This book is an instruction manual to use over time.

My number one goal is to help you to make big changes in your life to achieve excellent health, energy and happiness.

But this type of big change DOES NOT happen just by reading this book and it won't happen overnight. It will happen by using this book as a manual and by making small habit changes over time. A habit is something you do on a consistent basis. It is only through consistency that you will see your health, energy and happiness improve.

I will ask you this key question many times through the book:

"Which one, two or three small habit changes are you currently working on?" The habit changes you choose to work on will be specific to you. I will cover this in more depth in chapter two.

To achieve change, you simply need to focus on making a maximum of three positive habit changes per month.

How to use this book

Please read – it's the most important section in the book.

1. **Read the introduction** so you have a clear understanding of the current situation with today's lifestyle.

2. **Read the first chapter on how to change.** This will give you a good understanding of the challenges that come with making habit changes and the key ingredients to ensure your success.

3. **Read the second chapter on mindfulness.** This will give you a simple approach to mindfulness, so you can make this your natural way of living.

4. **You then have two options with the habit change sections:**

   A. Read all the habit change sections, then select the three habit changes you feel are most important and realistic for you, and focus on these for the next 30 days.

   Or

   B. Go to the section that focuses on the area of your life that is the most important to you right now. Then select the three habit changes you feel are the most important and realistic for you to focus on for the next 30 days.

5. **Choosing three habits to work on.** As you will see, there are more than 100 habits in this book and, when considering where to start, at first it might seem overwhelming.

Here is a simple exercise to help you decide which section or sections to focus on for your habit changes.

• Simply score out of 10 how satisfied you feel with the following areas of your life:

Evening habits to improve your sleep   /10

Morning habits to energise your day   /10

Work habits to maximise your creativity
and performance   /10

Nutrition habits for optimal health and energy   /10

Exercise habits to energise your mind and body   /10

Relaxation habits to calm your mind and body   /10

People habits for more positive relationships   /10

Everyday habits to create more happiness and success   /10

- Either pick the area of areas of your life in which you scored lowest, or pick the area or areas of your life that you feel inspired to improve.

- Now go to the section/sections in the book that relate to the area/areas you'd like to work on, and using your instinct, pick a maximum of three habit changes on which to focus over the next 30 days. Make sure your habit changes feel achievable and realistic for you.

6. **Some habits won't be right for you.** You will read certain habits that just won't feel appropriate for you. Be aware of this feeling as it means this particular habit is not right for you at the present time. In fact, some of the habits may never be right for you. This is fine as you will find plenty of habits that do feel right and these are the ones to work on.

Use this book
as your manual
to make continual
changes over time.

Everyone is unique
so don't feel you have
to do everything
in this book. Just focus
on the habits that
work for you.

An introduction
to health, energy
and happiness

There is no single approach that works for us all when it comes to health, energy and happiness. This is why you have to work out which ingredients will work for you.

However, there is one key message that is all-encompassing: "Your health, energy and happiness are ultimately driven by your daily and weekly habits."

It really is as simple as this:

Increase the daily and weekly habits that serve you.
Reduce the daily and weekly habits that don't serve you.

As you go through this process of habit change, you will feel your health, energy and happiness continually improve and this will encourage you to go further.

I truly believe that finding, and then living, the habits that serve your health, energy and happiness is a journey worth taking.

Over several years, I have discovered habits that work for most people. These habits are based on how your mind and body actually work.

You can take the contents of this book and use the elements that work for you.

You will find that making changes takes focus and time. You will learn how making a maximum of three small habit changes each month can be achievable and deliver fantastic results, making you healthier, more energised and happy.

The problem
with the modern
way of living

We've lost our balance and the modern way of living is taking us in the wrong direction for health, energy and happiness. In a nutshell, we have too many habits in our lives that don't serve us and not enough of the good habits. It is for this reason that it is "time for change".

There are two main reasons as to why we have lost our balance:

1. We are rarely fully present in this moment

Our minds are constantly drawn away from whatever we are doing in the present moment. The main causes of this are:

- Talking about the past or future.

- Thinking about the past or future.

- Technology distractions, e.g. smart phones, tablets and so on.

Of course, we engage in these from time to time, but most people are locked into one of these three almost all the time. People are rarely fully focused on what is happening right now which, as you will discover, has a dramatic impact on our health, energy and happiness.

2. Too many unhelpful habits

The second aspect of the problem is that we are increasingly making decisions that take us in the opposite direction to great health, energy and happiness. These small decisions turn into daily and weekly habits, which drive down health, energy and happiness.

So many of these decisions are made unconsciously.

Here are a few examples of habits that don't serve you, out of the hundreds of habits you will have in your life:

i) Being connected to technology in the evening, right up until you go to bed, which leads to poor sleep quality and low energy the next day.

ii) Eating nutritionally poor foods instead of nutritionally rich foods. This leads to poor health and energy in the long term.

iii) Regularly checking your smartphone. It is estimated that most people check their phone around 200 times or more per day. This continually draws your attention away from the present moment and affects your happiness, as well as your creativity and performance at work.

Chapter 1:
How to change

HEALTH, ENERGY AND HAPPINESS MADE SIMPLE

Your health, energy and happiness are driven by your daily and weekly habits.

Therefore, the formula to achieving great health, energy and happiness goes like this:

Increase the good habits in your life that have a positive effect on your health, energy and happiness.

Reduce those habits in your life that have a negative effect on your health, energy and happiness.

There are hundreds of habits that benefit your health, energy and happiness. The great news is that they are all simple.

So, with this straightforward formula, great health, energy and happiness should be easy to achieve, shouldn't it?

Well, as we know, that's not always the case. The challenge lies in making the habit changes and sticking to them. Habit change doesn't come easily, but there is a strategy for successful habit change.

Your health, energy and happiness are driven by your daily and weekly habits.

Increase the good habits and reduce the habits that don't serve you.

—

BRIDGING THE GAP BETWEEN KNOWING AND LIVING

The biggest mistake people make, when looking to improve their health, energy and happiness, is what I call the "more knowledge epidemic". You can get tricked into thinking more knowledge is the answer.

This is because access to information has never been easier. You can read magazines, self-help books, go on courses, watch YouTube videos and so on, but increasing your knowledge will not, in itself, improve your health, energy and happiness.

You have to take the knowledge and make sure it's sound – based on how your mind and body actually work. Then you have to bridge the gap between knowing something and living it, by taking that knowledge and turning it into daily and weekly habits in real life.

It is only when your knowledge has been translated into your habits that you will see your health, energy and happiness improve.

As well as cutting-edge content, this book offers clear principles for turning the information you collect into habits that you will be able to practise consistently.

So when reading each habit in this book, don't ask yourself whether you know the habit, ask yourself whether you practise the habit at least 80% of the time.

More knowledge
will not improve your
health, energy and
happiness.

It is only when
your knowledge
is translated into your
daily and weekly habits
that you will see your
health, energy and
happiness improve.

THREE FACTS ABOUT YOUR BRAIN THAT WILL CHANGE YOUR LIFE FOREVER

Research shows there are three facts about the brain that help us understand why habit change is such a challenge. These facts also allow you to understand how to achieve habit change.

FACT 1 - You can change the way your brain functions.

You can change your thoughts, beliefs and habits. This first fact is vital because many people don't believe they can change. When you understand that you can change, this will give you the belief and the confidence, which are essential for change.

FACT 2 - Change only happens when you consistently stretch yourself.

The reason this fact is so important is that most people underestimate how much commitment, motivation and focus is needed in the first 30 days to create a habit change. They therefore don't give the habit change enough focus and fall short. This can often reaffirm their belief that habit change is too hard or even impossible.

FACT 3 - The brain is naturally lazy.

The brain's job is to keep you alive and to conserve energy. So even if you put lots of hard work into changing a habit during the first 30 days, your lazy brain will be inclined to slip back into old habits after 30 days, unless you keep the momentum going for a further 60 days.

HABIT CHANGE MADE SIMPLE

Here is your framework for successful habit change.

Believe you can change

First and foremost, you need to believe you can change. Part of your belief can come from the fact that we can all create change in our lives by using these simple steps below.

Keep up the motivation and focus

You need motivation and focus throughout your first 30 days. This is the most challenging period during a habit change and your commitment is key.

Focus on three habit changes per month

Because of the level of commitment, focus and motivation needed for habit change, it is important to focus on a maximum of three habit changes per month.

Write down your habits

Writing down your habit changes can be really effective. Create a page in your note pad entitled "habit changes for my health, energy and happiness". Under this heading, write the month and year. Then write the three habits you will be working on that month. Complete this process each time you set your habit changes and regularly review your list of habit changes.

Example: Habit changes for my health, energy and happiness

June 2016
1. Avoid all technology an hour before bed.
2. Start each day with 20 minutes of meditation.
3. Before I start work, write down my three must do actions for my day.

July 2016
1. Swap coffee for Matcha tea in the mornings.
2. Three mornings a week, go to the gym for a 30-minute, high-intensity workout.
3. Include a high-protein food in each meal.

This process of writing down your habit changes, and reviewing them regularly, is highly beneficial. As with your goals, if you write them down and review them, you dramatically improve your chance of change.

Change your environment

Set yourself up for success by making changes to your environment that will support your habit change; for example, to help you drink 1.5 litres of water per day, buy a BPA-free water bottle (these bottles won't 'leak' plastic), fill it at the start of each day, and put it on your desk. Always shop for nutritionally rich foods (you will read more about these in the nutrition habits section) so your home is filled with healthy foods rather than processed foods. Put your gym clothes out by your bed ready for your morning exercise.

Use the 80/20 rule

In other words, don't expect to be perfect all the time, it just isn't realistic. As long as you practise a good habit 80% of the time, you will be gaining the benefits from that habit. For example, I don't eat any dairy products — no milk or cheese; however I LOVE dark chocolate so I have this occasionally and it contains a small amount of milk.

Reward your success

Fuel positive change by giving yourself good feedback each time you complete your habit and reward yourself (something that brings you pleasure while also being healthy, such as a massage or beauty treatment, or dinner at your favourite healthy restaurant) after your first 30 days. Research shows this simple reward practice has a huge impact on the success of your habit changes over time.

Imbed your habits

To imbed your new habits fully, keep focused for your first 90 days. During this 90-day period, you can also introduce new habits. Remember only to implement a maximum of three new habits per month, though.

Be aware of dormant habits

Be aware of the dormant habits syndrome. After your first 90 days of focus on a habit, you will find most habits are cemented into your life. But there are certain bad habits that can lie dormant and which return if you choose to let them in.

The bad habits that lie dormant, and those that are gone forever, will be unique to each person. Maybe yours are smoking, excess coffee, sugar, or being inconsistent with exercise. Whatever your poor habits might be, be aware of them and give them extra focus. This basic awareness and extra focus is often enough to keep you on track.

Find the time

Lack of time is by far the most common reason people give for not being able to put a new habit in place is time. But having coached thousands of people, many of whom are extremely busy, I know the issue is never really time. It's simply a case of prioritisation and tailoring. If you truly want the benefits that come from meditation, and you prioritise to make this happen, you will find the time. Maybe you see the benefits of morning exercise, so you prioritise an early night three evenings a week to ensure you have time in the morning.

In terms of tailoring, here's an example: it may be challenging to visit the gym in the morning and fit in a one-hour workout; however, you can tailor your morning workout to fit your limited time. For example, choose one of the 20-minute morning workouts from the exercise section on page 138 to do at home. I'm sure you agree your health, energy and happiness are a priority, so I urge you to take action.

Remember that habit change is a habit

The final point to make about habit change is that once you've been using these steps for about six months, they will become effortless and second nature, like a habit itself.

Habit change in a nutshell

Set a maximum of three habit changes per month.

Give these habits your commitment and focus for 30 days and keep focused for a further 60 days. The rest of the habit-change framework is there to give you the full knowledge of habit change to support your success.

FOCUS ON MARGINAL GAINS

The habit change framework is your basis for change.

In addition, the marginal gains philosophy works really well in conjunction with habit change.

This philosophy is a mindset of continual improvement; in particular, it focuses on very small steps of ongoing improvement.

Health, energy and happiness will not be achieved overnight, following one big action or motivational speech. They are achieved by cultivating mindfulness and by making positive decisions and habit changes over time.

Focus on a
maximum of three
habits per month.

Keep focused
on your habits for
90 days to fully imbed
your new habits.

This philosophy of small steps and continual improvement is a further layer within habit change. Although your habit changes should be simple and achievable, these small improvements can take place every day.

This philosophy is used in most professional sports; for example, the highly successful British cycling team at the 2012 London Olympics used the marginal gains philosophy to great effect, winning eight gold medals at the games. The team studied all the elements that can impact on performance – from the bike design, to the pillow the cyclists use to achieve great sleep. They then looked to make ongoing improvements to all of these elements. Small, continual improvements, over time, add up to a big overall improvement in performance.

As with any philosophy, this is a mindset for how to live your life.

LOOK OUT FOR SMALL DAILY IMPROVEMENTS IN YOUR LIFE

Here are some examples:

- Go to bed 10 minutes earlier than normal.

- Swap rice for quinoa.

- Reduce your spoonful of sugar in your coffee to half a spoonful.

- Swap one of your evening workouts for a morning workout.

- Turn off your phone for 20 minutes while you eat lunch.

- Wake up 10 minutes earlier and do a five-minute guided meditation.

- Read this book for five minutes each evening.

- Write down your most important actions today and spend your first 30 minutes of the day on this action.

BECOMING SKILLED AT KNOWING YOUR MIND AND BODY

As you will see, throughout this book, there are a number of areas of your life in which to make habit changes and, within these areas, there are many different habits to address.

Given that you only want to change a maximum of three habits each month, the big question is: where to start?

This is where it becomes important to listen to your instinct and your body.

Inside of you is a well of untapped wisdom. The more in touch you become with your mind and body, the more you will know what needs to change and you will find the unhelpful habits fall away from your life. Here are two simple strategies to help you grow more in tune with what's right for you:

1. Follow the steps on page 54 in the 'listen to your instinct' section. This will enable you to tap into your subconscious mind or, as I prefer to call it, your gut instinct.

2. Start to become more aware of the feelings you get from the things you do. How do you feel when you have certain foods or drinks? How do you feel sitting down without any movement? How do you feel when you do certain forms of exercise? How do you feel when you speak positively about your life?

If something feels helpful and good for you, such as talking positively, taking part in morning exercise or eating lots of vegetables, then do more of this. Equally, if you can feel something isn't serving you (such as the morning after drinking a bottle of wine) then, next time, just have one or two glasses.

This is a skill you need to learn, so the more often you practise listening to your instinct and body, the more in-tune with yourself you will become.

Start by taking the time to think and feel which areas of your life you want to improve and which three habits are the most important, beneficial and achievable for you at this point in time.

BE YOUR BEST FRIEND

Before we get into the changes that will bring you great health, energy and happiness, there is an important point to make about your motivation.

This can be summed up by the simple question: who is your best friend?

Your first answer may be your closest friend, or maybe your brother or sister, your mother or father. However, the answer everyone should give to this question is: "me"– themselves.

Over the years, I've been lucky enough to meet some amazing people who would do anything for their friends and family. The strange thing is that, although they have so much love for their family and friends, they often don't have that same level of love for themselves.

As with all the habits in this book, it's important not only to know that you are your best friend, but actually to live like you are your best friend.

This one simple belief has a huge impact on your motivation and how you live your life. Think of it like this: do you want your family and closest friends to be healthy, energised and happy? Of course you do and you would do anything to support them in achieving this.

So do the same for yourself, with these three simple beliefs:

1. I am my best friend.

2. Given that I am my best friend, I obviously want to be healthy, energised and happy.

3. I am therefore committed and motivated to making myself healthy, energised and happy by practising mindfulness and by being aware of the decisions I make, so I can adopt more of the habits that benefit my health, energy and happiness.

Chapter 2:
The key to health, energy and happiness

THE NUMBER ONE HABIT FOR HEALTH, ENERGY AND HAPPINESS

I'm often asked: "Out of all of the daily habits to improve health, energy and happiness, which is the number one habit that has the biggest impact?"

My answer is always "mindfulness", and it is number one by a long way. However, there are some initial problems with mindfulness for most people.

THE CHALLENGES PEOPLE FACE WHEN IMPLEMENTING MINDFULNESS

1. Mindfulness originated from Buddhism more than 2,000 years ago and consequently has a spiritual element, upon which many mindfulness books focus. This can turn off many people .

2. Many mindfulness books overcomplicate this way of living, by talking a lot about the concept but failing to give simple, practical actions for applying the approach.

3. Most importantly, these books often fail to give you a system for changing to this new way of living. Change does not come easy, so understanding how to achieve simple habit changes is essential.

A SIMPLE APPROACH TO MINDFULNESS

Mindfulness can give you a totally new way in which to live, which completely changes what happens in your life, and more importantly, how you feel about what happens.

This simple approach to mindfulness has two key elements.

PART 1. Do one thing at a time and give it 100% of your focus.

Whatever you're doing, whether working on your laptop, eating, talking, cooking, exercising, meditating, reading this book, having a shower, hugging or anything else, give that one thing all your focus; do one thing at a time.

PART 2. Become more aware of the decisions you make.

When your awareness is fully in this moment, it helps you to make decisions that serve your health, energy and happiness positively.

When your awareness is not fully in this moment, you find yourself running on a conditioned autopilot where, more often than not, your decisions do not serve you.

Many of our decisions are made unconsciously. This can be driven by our environment, our life's conditioning or the millions of pieces of data being processed by our brains on a daily basis.

Making decisions, every day, that serve you is vital.

Your decisions turn into your daily and weekly habits, and your habits are the biggest drivers of your health, energy and happiness.

Here are three examples of decisions you can make that serve you:

1. Talk positively about yourself to enhance your happiness and success.

2. Improve the quality of the time you spend with family and friends by turning off your phone off when you are with them.

3. Give your body at least 20 minutes of exercise each morning.

REPETITION

When my editor first read this book, one of her comments was "you advise people to do one thing at a time with all their focus many times in this chapter. I think you need to reduce this, there's too much repetition".

I was glad she had noticed, but there is a good reason for this. In my experience, repetition is essential. In fact, I guarantee that many people will read this chapter and, even with the repetition, will fail to make the shift. So I'm giving you advance warning that I will repeat this phrase a lot of times to help increase the chances that you will own it at a deep level and will start to do one thing at a time with all your focus.

Do one thing at
a time and give it
your 100% focus.

Have your full
awareness in this
moment, so you
can make better
decisions that serve
your health, energy
and happiness.

THE 80/20 RULE

With most things in life, there are normally one or two really important, big things that make up 80% of your success. For example, with weight loss, eating the right foods at the right time will make up roughly 80% of your success. This really is the case with mindfulness.

I remember going through years of practice to try to master the many elements of mindfulness, but I never felt I was getting anywhere and it always felt so confusing. Over time, I realised that if I just mastered the following, then 80% of my work would be complete, the rest I could fine-tune over time.

"I do one thing at a time and give it my 100% focus. I have my full awareness in this moment so I can make decisions that serve me and, in turn, help me create more habits that benefit my health, energy and happiness."

I urge you to do the same: put all your focus into mastering doing one thing at a time with all your focus and having your full awareness in this moment so you can make better decisions.

The information in the rest of this chapter is just that extra 20% that gives you additional support to make mindfulness effortless and effective.

THE BENEFITS OF MINDFULNESS

We've covered the two key elements of mindfulness, so what are the benefits of adopting this new way of living?

As you will see from what follows, there are so many benefits. In fact, you will find it extremely hard, if not impossible, to discover anything that has more benefits for your health, energy and happiness than mindfulness.

I could talk all day about the evidence for each of these benefits, but here are a few of the reasons why mindfulness has an impact. Mindfulness:

Energises your life. Everything becomes more vibrant. How often have you been for a walk in the countryside and not noticed the beauty around you because you were lost in thought about the past or future?

Helps you to make decisions that serve you. For example, you are always aware to walk up the stairs and not take the lift.

Increases your gratitude for life. You find yourself saying "thank you" for small, yet important, things in life.

Improves happiness, giving you a sense of calm. How can you not be happy and calm when you are fully enjoying the present moment?

Increases your compassion for yourself, others and the planet. When you become aware of the beauty around you, you treasure it.

Improves the quality of all the relationships in your life.
For example, it is only when we truly listen to a person that we
fully connect and properly respond.

Increases your health and energy levels. Your energy
becomes dedicated to one thing at a time and isn't so drained
by technology and repetitive thinking.

Improves sleep. In 2008, I went through a period where I
was presenting a lot of workshops and I became so over-
stimulated that I developed sleep problems. It was thanks
to both (TM) transcendental meditation (a meditation
technique I cover later in the book), which helped to reduce
this stimulation and mindfulness, which helped to reduce the
worry, that I started to regain my balance and sleep well again.

**Helps you become skilled at listening and following
your instincts.** The more you are fully in this moment and
able to listen to your own instincts, the more these will speak
to you and the more you will learn to trust them.

Makes you more successful in work. Professional sports
people have found that the more you focus on one thing at a
time, with all your attention, the better you will perform and
the more success you will have.

Improves problem solving and creativity. By applying your
full focus to a problem, or anything you want to create, you
tap into the true source of all creativity.

**Lowers your blood pressure and boosts your immune
system.** By living in the present moment, you live with more
peace and calm.

Reduces negative emotions, stress, anxiety, fear and anger.
As you will read on page 56, a key part of mindfulness is
acceptance, and through acceptance, negative emotions reduce.

Improves your resilience to pressure. Better decisions are
made, better habits are created, a stronger mindset is adopted
and resilience increases.

By doing one thing at a time, giving it your 100% focus and
by having your full awareness in this moment, you can make
decisions that serve you. These simple changes allow you to
tap into all these amazing benefits.

Which of these benefits would you really love? Use this as
your motivation for keeping focused on making this change.

YOUR ULTIMATE PRIORITY FOR MINDFULNESS

Remember these two elements are your highest priority and if you only master these, you are 80% there with mindfulness.

Do one thing at a time

As I've mentioned, the essence of mindfulness is doing one thing at a time with all your focus. This will bring about all the great benefits of mindfulness.

Have your full awareness in this moment

Practise having your full awareness in this moment by giving all your attention to what you are doing right now. This will help you to make better decisions that serve you.

EXTRA ELEMENTS OF MINDFULNESS

These are extra elements of mindfulness that you can work on over time.

Understanding your thoughts

For most people, thoughts arise on a continuous and involuntary basis. Positive thoughts about your life, and about how you feel your life will evolve, can be extremely helpful. But so much of our thinking is repetitive, negative or unimportant. The great news is that you have the ability to reduce this habitual thinking massively and also to change the impact your thoughts have on your life.

Thoughts come and go and if you attach importance to these thoughts and believe all of them to be true, they will not be of help to your life.

Practise this new habit of not taking your thoughts so seriously – just let them pass by like clouds in the sky. You become the watcher of your thoughts and you are not lost deep within them.

Having your full focus on doing one thing at a time will help your thoughts to move into the background instead of being the dominant element in your life.

As with all habits, this new habit will take time and awareness. But the energy you invest in this will change your life, and more importantly, change how you feel about your life.

Managing your emotions

Just like thoughts, emotions can also consume us and take us away from our practice of doing one thing at a time with all our focus.

Emotions are simply your reactions to your thoughts. By not taking your thoughts so seriously and just letting them pass by, you stop the chain reaction from thoughts to emotions.

I'm not saying this will mean you never feel emotions, of course you will; they're part of life and positive emotions such as love, excitement, peace and joy are some of life's most beautiful experiences. However, by bringing your full awareness into this moment, you can reduce negative, unhelpful and unnecessary emotions such as worry, anger, jealousy, fear, guilt and frustration.

As with thoughts, the habit of watching your emotions and letting them pass, is a tremendously powerful habit to cultivate. Again, this requires your awareness to be fully in this moment so that you can observe the emotions, instead of being consumed by them.

Focus on your breath

Whenever you can, pause for 30 seconds and get in tune with your breath. You can do this at any time during the day. Just breathe slowly – in through your nose and out through your nose – for 30 seconds, and during this time, give all your focus to the air going in through your nose and out through your nose. The air we breathe is truly a gift to consider and appreciate. This simple process will also help to calm you from all the stimulation of your day.

Focus on your senses

Take a pause and choose one of your senses: smell, taste, touch, hearing or sight. Once you have chosen a sense, give all your focus to whatever you are doing through that sense. For example, if you are eating, focus on the taste of your food and nothing else. This simple habit is a great access point for bringing all your awareness into the present moment.

Flow with life

When you are fully in this moment, thoughts become part of the background. Your main focus is not on your thoughts but on whatever you are doing in this moment. When this happens, you are able to flow better with life, which brings amazing situations and people into your life. Being 'in flow' is a much easier and happier way to live than trying to control everything and then growing frustrated when things don't go to plan.

Listen to your instinct

It is very easy to get lost in your thoughts and believe them to be the truth on which you have to base your decisions.

When your awareness is fully in the moment and thoughts become nothing more than background noise, you can start to make decisions based on instinct.

The more often you tune into your gut instinct, the more it will speak to you; the more you follow it, the more you will find that your instinct is right.

A very simple habit I've used to great effect to help me access my instinct, comprises three simple steps:

1. I sit in a quiet place where I won't be disturbed, and I close my eyes, relax and focus on my breathing. I stay in this place until I can feel my thoughts are fading into the background and my full awareness is on my breath.

2. I then ask myself a question that relates to the decision I need to make and I make this a closed question, it only has a yes or no answer. For example: "Should I work with this person, yes or no?"

3. I always get a 100% "yes" or a 100% "no". I then go with whatever the answer is; if it's yes, I do it, if it's no, I don't.

Over the past seven years I have gone against my instinct only once, and – guess what – it was a mess!

By using this process, I am not analysing the situation with my limited conscious mind. I am tapping into the wealth of knowledge, data and wisdom within my far greater subconscious mind.

Practise relaxed focus

When you focus on one thing at a time, do it in a relaxed, calm way. My personal favourite example of this approach is Roger Federer playing tennis. He's 100% focused, exuding a sense of relaxed calm.

See life with fresh eyes

When you are truly focused on everything in this moment, you will start to see things as if for the first time, with fresh eyes. Observe children because they are a great example of this in action.

Avoid making judgements

If, on occasion, this moment is not ideally what you want (maybe you are at work and not loving the task on which you are working), avoid judging this moment and adding negative commentary.

Cultivate acceptance

"Cultivate acceptance." I remember that when I first heard this concept explained, I thought: "I'm not accepting things that are not going to plan."

But over time, I recognised the madness of my thinking. What is happening right now is happening, so it is much better to accept this moment as it is than to fight it. Acceptance is not an absence of action. You can have peace with acceptance of this moment as it is, but then choose, in a calm, focused way, the action to take to move forward.

Remember, what you resist will persist and grow stronger. Next time you find yourself in a situation that is not ideal, practise acceptance and feel the peace it brings.

Practise patience

The constant feeling that the future will be better than now creates, in some, a state of continuous impatience to get to the next moment. The trouble is that when we get there, we invariably feel that the next moment will be even better, so we are never fully here, right now.

Yes, plans for the future can be exciting, but by being impatient to get there, you will lose the magic of this moment, and in turn, lose the magic of life. Next time you find yourself growing impatient, see if you can accept the speed as it is. This is not to be confused with a reduction in your determination – you can still go after the things you want in life with full power – but know when patience is needed and relax with the natural flow of things. For some personality types, patience can be a constant challenge, but as with all habits, this takes practice, and slowly, over time, you can make improvements in this area.

Trust in life

How many people have said to you: "Everything is happening for a reason, trust that it will all be ok?" We all know this makes sense. The key is to cultivate this trust so you actually 'live it' rather than simply agreeing with the statement. Trusting that this moment is exactly how it should be brings a great sense of calm into your life. As with all habits, it takes time to feel comfortable with this, but it will eventually become your natural way.

Enjoy the process

It can be easy to defer your enjoyment until everything gets done. You rush through your tasks believing everything will be great at the end. But with this way of living, there is never an end. Instead, enjoy the journey by bringing your full attention into each daily task.

Practise gratitude

This point is probably one of the most important of all. Whatever this moment is, be grateful for it. After all, every day of your life is precious. My favourite example of this comes from Bali, the place in which I lived for seven months while writing this book.

The people there are the most wonderful people; they don't have many of the things we value in the West, but they are grateful for the simple things in life such as health, family, friends, community and nature. This gratitude, each day, for the simple things in life, makes the Balinese people shine with happiness, something from which we can learn so much. In addition, research in the area of positive psychology shows that writing a daily list of three things for which you are grateful is one of the best habits for happiness.

What, where, when and how often to practise mindfulness?

Here are the common questions that arise with mindfulness and the answers to these questions:

In which areas of my life can I practise mindfulness?

You can practise mindfulness in any area of your life, be it work, relationships, your hobbies, while having a shower – the list is endless. The practice of doing one thing at a time, and doing it with all your focus, can apply to every aspect of your life.

Where and when can I practise mindfulness?

The beauty of mindfulness is that you don't have to go to a class or be in a certain place at a certain time. You can practise it wherever you are and whenever you want.

How often, and for how long, should I practise mindfulness?

When you start doing one thing at a time with all your focus, the duration is not so important. Even 20 seconds can bring you amazing benefits. The key is consistency and regularity throughout the day.

Your mindfulness tipping point

There's a good rule to remember with all things related to health, energy and happiness: "Your life will attract more of the same." For example, if you are eating unhealthy foods, you will naturally be attracted to eating more unhealthy foods.

If your mind is constantly distracted by technology, or you are often lost in thought about the past or future, you will naturally be drawn to more of the same.

This also applies to mindfulness. The more often you do one thing at a time with all your focus, the more often this will happen.

Over time, a tipping point occurs, so you will find yourself in the moment, focused on one thing at a time, more often than you are lost in thought or distracted by technology. This is your tipping point. You've trained yourself to live fully in this moment and it is a wonderful place.

Remember, this won't happen overnight, but all you really need to focus on is this moment.

One habit change that makes mindfulness simple

A daily meditation practice can make mindfulness simple. The key difference between meditation and mindfulness is that meditation is best done in a quiet place with your eyes closed. This allows you to focus fully on one thing, without any distractions and, in the process, deeply relax your mind and body.

Mindfulness won't bring about the same level of relaxation as meditation but mindfulness can be performed anywhere, at any time.

Whatever type of meditation you practise, you will be bringing your full awareness into this moment; this is essentially creating a new connection in your brain and training yourself to do one thing at a time with all your focus. You are then able to transfer this experience into all areas of your life.

There are many types of meditation practice, so you need to find what works for you.

Here is my personal meditation experience: I had tried many meditation practices over the years, but after much research, I realised transcendental meditation (TM) was something very different to anything I'd done in the past. So in 2007, I took a weekend course of instruction in TM, which I found was very easy to learn.

During the course, you are given a mantra specific to you. This mantra is yours for the rest of your life. The practice of TM is to sit with your eyes closed and to repeat the mantra in your head. As you repeat the mantra, you transcend into deep relaxation and your thoughts fade into the background.

Since starting TM, I have never looked back. The impact it has had on my energy, performance, sleep and creativity has been amazing.

This one, simple, effortless, natural technique allows you to go beyond thinking, and access the deep source of all your energy, creativity and intelligence, dissolving stress and enriching mind, body, emotions and relationships.

In terms of the most effective habit for a healthy and happy mind, meditation – and for me, TM meditation – is number one. TM brings all the same benefits as mindfulness, the big difference is that TM takes you into a deeply relaxed state; so relaxed, in fact, that your brain waves slow down to the same level as that of deep sleep.

As well as all these great benefits, TM can make mindfulness simple. For more information on TM, see reading list at the end of the book.

Understanding past and future

You have three options for where to focus your mind:

1. You can think about the past.

2. You can think about the future.

Or

3. You can put all your focus into this moment and enjoy it to the fullest. When you take this option, your thoughts will fade into the background as your main focus is on this moment.

The fact is, most people, most of the time, are either thinking about the past or the future. Some dwell in the past, while others are more drawn to the future.

The other variable in this equation is whether your thoughts of the past or future are positive or negative.

To think about events from the past that bring you negativity will not serve you. You've already experienced the event, so why relive it in this moment and bring yourself further pain? Just as unhelpful as reliving a past negative event is worrying about what could go wrong in the future. A great quote from author Mark Twain, to which I'm sure you can relate, describes this perfectly: "I've been through some terrible times in my life, some of which actually happened."

So we've established that it's not helpful to think about negative past events or worry about potential future events. But what about thinking about past positive events or potential positive future events?

There are some benefits to thinking about past positive events occasionally. This can bring you pleasure in this moment and help motivate you for the future. Also, thinking about the future is important at times, as it allows us to plan. Visualising how you want things to go can help bring about positive feelings and success.

So, apart from some occasional positive past and future thinking, you really want your mind fully focused on this moment. After all, this moment is the only real moment in your life.

Given this, here are a few simple principles to apply:

1. Discipline yourself to avoid all negative thinking about the past, and all worrying about the future.

2. Use the 80/20 rule for present moment focus, versus positive past and future thinking: 80% of the time, do one thing at a time and fully focus your mind on this moment. Then, 20% of the time, you can think about positive events in the past, or plan and visualise positive events in the future.

Obviously, this will never be exact, you just want a general sense that most of your focus is in this moment.

That all sounds pretty simple right? Well it's easy to say but very few people are living their lives this way. As I've mentioned, the more often you bring your full attention into this moment, the more this will be your natural default, and the more natural it becomes, the greater the benefits of mindfulness that you will experience.

Goal setting without getting lost in the future

Something with which I personally struggled for many years was a tendency to get lost in the future. I've always been very ambitious, not just ambitious with work, but ambitious in all areas of my life. This led to a preoccupation with setting goals.

The challenge I had, which is a common problem with goal setting, was getting trapped in, what I call, the "when then game"; in other words "when I have my new house then I'll be happy", "when my Italian is fluent, then I'll feel I've achieved something", "when I've met the perfect partner, then everything will be great".

This means that happiness is continually deferred until a time when the goal or goals have been achieved. The tragedy of this approach is that, by the time the goals are achieved, we've already set the next set of goals.

This means too many people are never fully happy in this moment and it also means the 80/20 rule has become the 20/80 rule: 20% of your focus is on this moment and 80% on the goals you've set.

So how can you set goals to help you to be the best you can be, and progress your life, while still living in this moment?

Here are my rules for goal setting, to ensure the goals you set keep all areas of your life progressing, while also practising mindfulness.

I have found this formula not only ensures your focus is on this moment 80% of the time, but also dramatically improves the results you achieve in relation to your goals.

One of the biggest reasons people don't achieve important goals is that they grow overwhelmed by the size of the challenge. The following process helps you to break down your goals into small, achievable actions.

Your goal-setting framework

What positive feelings do you love?

I've had goals in the past where something about them has felt wrong, but I didn't know why. I've also set goals where my feelings of excitement have been extreme. So why is this?

We all want to experience certain feelings in life. In fact, our feelings are just as important as the goal itself. There are hundreds of positive feelings and the feelings that are most important to you will be unique to you.

So before you start looking at goals, it's important to establish which feelings you love most in life. Once you are clear about these feelings, you can set goals that bring about these feelings. Equally, if a goal does not bring about one or more of these feelings, you'll know it's not the right goal for you.

Here's a simple process to discover the feelings you love:

- Take some time, now, to list as many positive feelings as you can that you truly love to experience.

- List your top three-to-five feelings.

- With this process, you can group certain feelings together, so that when they are combined, they sum up the overall feeling you love.

- Write these feelings in your note pad.

To give an example, here are my top three feelings and some examples of how these feelings drive my goals:

1. Love

The feeling of love is what I desire most. I can experience this feeling of love for myself, my family, friends, partner, my team at work, my community and animals. I therefore set goals that allow me to experience more love.

2. Excited, energised and passionate

These three feelings are very powerful in my life and I therefore set goals that can help me feel more excited, energised and passionate. I love setting challenging work goals that excite me. I love setting goals where I can have new adventures, work from different places and connect with new, inspiring people. All these things make me excited and passionate. As you can imagine, I also love to work on my health and energy as this gives me an energised feeling.

3. Inspired, light and free

The first of these three feelings is important for me, both in terms of work, but also in terms of creating a great life outside of work. For me, when I set a goal, I look at it and question if it really inspires me. If the answer is "yes", great; if the answer is "no", then I know I need a different or more stretching goal. Feeling light and free is also linked to my feeling of being inspired. I have to feel a lightness and a sense of freedom with my goals. If a goal inspires me and brings me a feeling of success, but it feels heavy or I feel trapped by the goal, then I know it's not right.

Remember, the feelings you choose will be unique to you. It may take you some time to work out the feelings that you love most; however I can promise you it will be worth it.

As you go through the rest of these goal-setting steps, ensure that each goal you set brings about at least one of your top feelings.

Brainstorm what you would love in all the key areas of life

To set your long-term goals, use a simple creative brainstorming exercise. Think big and think about what you would love to achieve in your life in these eight key areas. Make sure you then cross-check that the goals you come up with generate the feelings you desire:

1. Health
2. Family
3. Friends
4. Relationship
5. Work
6. Home
7. Hobbies
8. Finance

This exercise is designed to bring out all of your ideas and, from there, you can identify goals that really inspire and excite you.

Next, jot down your goals in your note pad. You may do nothing about some of these goals for many years, then one day you'll decide to take action. For example, one of my long-term goals was to write a book. I had this on my list for many years, but it just wasn't the right time. Then one day, I was inspired to take action and six months later, I had written my first book, *EnergiseYou*.

Prioritise your three-month goals

Look at your long-term goals and decide which three goals you most want to achieve over the next three months. Make these goals as specific as possible so you can measure them at the end of your three months, then write down these goals in your note pad.

One-month actions

Consider your three-month goals and set actions just for the month ahead. These are the actions that are the most appropriate for progressing you towards achieving your three-month goals. Then write these in your note pad.

Daily focus

At the beginning of each day, write down your three 'must dos' for the day. These are the most important three things for the day that will move you towards achieving your one-month actions.

Do one thing at a time

The final part is putting mindfulness into action. Take the most important of your three 'must dos' for the day and focus fully on that action; do that one thing with all your focus.

Remember, big goals are never achieved in one big action, they are achieved via one small goal at a time and small goals are achieved far more effectively when you do one thing at a time with all your focus.

Take calm, fearless action

One final challenge, that everyone has to overcome when achieving their goals, is fear. Our minds create fear by getting lost in the past or future.

Feeling paralysed by fear is one of the biggest roadblocks to living the life you are meant to live. Fear itself can become a habit over time.

Equally, you can create a new habit by cultivating a calm, fearless approach to your goals.

There are five very simple strategies for managing and removing fear:

1. Adopt the belief that you are calm and fearless. To achieve this belief, start by deciding that this is your belief. If you say something to yourself often enough, you'll believe it, for example: "Whenever I approach something new and challenging I'm calm and fearless."

2. Follow the goal-setting framework described earlier in the chapter. By breaking down your goals into smaller goals and simple actions, you remove a huge amount of fear.

3. Do one thing at a time with all your focus. When your mind is fully in this moment, you dramatically reduce the feeling of fear.

4. Be comfortable with doing things that have some element of fear. The more often you do things that cause an element of fear, the more you will become comfortable with fear and create a new habit of facing things that generate fear.

5. Practise, practise, practise. The simple steps are always the best. The more you practise something you fear, the more you increase your confidence and reduce fear. Public speaking is a great example.

Turn off your phone to practise mindfulness

This simple habit can make the pursuit of mindfulness so much easier. Imagine playing tennis with a heavy rucksack on your back. You just wouldn't do it because it would get in the way and affect your chances of playing well.

The same applies to practising mindfulness while your phone is switched on; it really does make it extremely challenging.

I mentioned that the three biggest reasons people struggle to do one thing at a time, with all their focus, are thinking about the past, thinking about the future and/or being distracted by technology – in particular, phones.

You cannot remove your mind but you can remove your phone, thereby removing one of the three big distractions.

Here are four habits on which to focus:

1. Avoid turning on your phone for the first couple of hours of the day.
2. Turn off your phone for the couple of hours before you go to sleep.
3. Give yourself 'phone breaks' throughout the day by turning off your phone for at least 30 minutes at a time. This could be while you have lunch with a friend, while you go for

a walk, or when you are working on an important project.

4. The aformentioned habits are key, but you also need to build in longer breaks. Go on a phone detox for at least 24 hours as often as you can. This could be for a day, a weekend or a whole week's holiday without your phone.

The other key change to make with your phone that will support your mindfulness practice is reducing the number of things you use it for. Yes, email and texting can make you more efficient with your time, but what can you dump today? Twitter, Instagram, Pinterest, Facebook, dating websites, apps, games?

This list goes on, and it will keep growing. It's no wonder we are on our phones so much of the time with so many apps to keep us distracted. Take control today and go minimal.

It really does make mindfulness easier when you reduce what you use your phone for. Also avoid taking your phone everywhere and turn it off more often. These simple changes will literally transform your life. I dare you!

Turn off your phone
for the first and last
hour of each day.

Give yourself
breaks from your
phone throughout
the day, in the
evenings, on weekends
and on holiday.

Remember to practise

The final piece of the puzzle is probably the most important. As you can see, the key part of mindfulness is doing one thing at a time with all your focus. The challenge is that this is not our habit. Our habit is to be continually distracted away from this moment.

If I sat next to you and said, "whatever you are doing right now, just do that and only that, and give it all your focus", you could focus and do it. The challenge is to maintain the awareness – to remember to live in this way.

Here are some simple actions you could take to help you remember to do one thing at a time more often:

- Make the login password on your computer something that reminds you to do one thing at a time with all your focus, for instance, 'one thing'.

- When you note down your goals, always write this at the top of your list: "Do one thing at a time with all my focus".

- Commit, with a friend or with your partner, to practise mindfulness when you are eating lunch or dinner. Turn off your phones and give your full attention to each other and nothing else.

- Start by committing to one activity or task in which you will always practise mindfulness. It may be your morning shower, brushing your teeth, your morning Matcha tea or your yoga class.

- Read this chapter often as a reminder to keep on track.

- Start your day by doing one thing at a time with all your focus, with 20 minutes of meditation as soon as you wake up.

SUMMARY

The question that often occurs to people when they start practising mindfulness is "am I doing it right?"

The simple answer is that you are 80% there if:

1. You are doing one thing at a time with all your focus so you enjoy life to the fullest.

2. Your full awareness is on this moment, thereby helping you make more positive decisions that serve you.

Everything else is just fine tuning based on the extra elements in this chapter. It really is that simple.

Chapter 3:
Your foundation

YOUR CURRENT SITUATION AND SOLUTION

To summarise: you now have the foundation to start, or continue, your journey to greater health, energy and happiness.

Your current situation

You have a good understanding of your current situation and the problem with the modern way of living. We are constantly distracted from the present moment and increasingly make decisions that take us in the wrong direction for health, energy and happiness.

Your solution

You now have a good understanding of why creating change in your life can be challenging, but with the right framework, change is achievable. You understand that mindfulness is the key habit to living life to the fullest in this moment, by simply doing one thing at a time with all your focus.

You also understand that, by being more aware and present in this moment, you are able to make better, conscious decisions and therefore develop habits that serve you.

So you understand the problem with the modern way of living, and armed with the framework for habit change and a simple approach to mindfulness, you are now ready to start changing your habits. The remainder of this book is designed to walk you through the key areas of your life, detailing all the best habits that serve your health, energy and happiness.

Chapter 4:
Your habit changes

In this chapter, I walk you through all the most positive habits you can develop, in the key areas of your life. Remember only to focus on three new habits per month. Use your instinct to decide which habits feel most suitable and achievable right now.

EVENING HABITS TO ACHIEVE GREAT SLEEP

INTRODUCTION

The way you spend your evenings is fundamental to your health, energy and happiness. Not only do you want to ensure your evenings are fulfilling, but also that you use this time to prepare yourself in a natural way for quality sleep.

Given that quality sleep makes up one third of your life, it really is your foundation for health, energy and happiness. Good sleep enables your cells to repair, allows the brain to process the day and is key to balancing your hormones. It is essential to practise positive evening habits to achieve great sleep so you awake refreshed and re-energised.

THE CHALLENGE

Here are some poor evening habits that are all too common:

- You are so tired from your day that most evenings are spent passed out in front of the TV.

- You are still half working in the evening by thinking about work or checking your emails on your phone.

- You work so late that you barely have an evening to speak of.

The biggest cause of poor sleep today is over-stimulation of our minds and bodies. The three biggest causes of this over-stimulation are:

- **City life.** If you live and work in a big city you will be exposed to a great deal of stimulation.

- **Volume.** The sheer volume of activities we cram into our lives, with every minute filled with something, has an over-stimulating effect.

- **Technology.** Most people are switched on to some form of technology from the moment they wake until the moment they go to bed. This is highly stimulating.

THE SOLUTION

The first element of the solution is to be proactive in organising your evenings so that they become more rich and fulfilling.

The second is to put in place the core evening habits that will calm your mind and body after the stimulation of the day. This will help you to fall asleep effortlessly and importantly, it will ensure you achieve high sleep quality.

The benefit of high sleep quality is that you will awake refreshed and re-energised and will have the strong foundation for health, energy and happiness during the day ahead.

'Brain dump' your day to create peace

Creating a sense of peace in your mind not only helps you switch off from work but also allows you to enjoy your evening, free of worry.

This habit is particularly useful if you find yourself thinking about work during the evening, or worse, in bed, just as you try to sleep.

To achieve this at the end of your working day, in the workplace, on the way home, or when you get in from work, 'brain dump the day' by writing down any actions for work and any challenges you have, with possible solutions.

Once you have this written down, accept that nothing more can be done with it today and commit to addressing work again the following day.

Create a partition between work and non-work

The old adage that "all work and no play makes Jack a dull boy" is correct. If your life is all about work and you don't give yourself time to switch off, then you don't fully re-charge. Your life may feel out of balance and it can lead to burn out. It will also affect your performance, productivity and creativity the next day.

Ensure you switch off from work by creating a clear partition between work and non-work time. So, if you finish work at 6pm one day and start work again the following morning at

9am, ensure you stay away from work during the rest of the time to re-charge your mind and, importantly, to enjoy your non-work time.

Minimise stimulation

As I mentioned in the introduction, modern life over-stimulates our minds and bodies. It is therefore important to minimise further stimulation in the evening, to ensure you are able to achieve quality sleep. The key things to avoid in the evening are:

- Intense exercise
- Caffeine
- Foods and drinks high in sugar
- Excessive alcohol
- Excessive technology use

Organise your people time

Your evenings are a great opportunity to spend quality time with the important people in your life, whether that's family, friends or your partner. This habit gives you the perfect opportunity to practise the essence of mindfulness.

Do one thing at a time with all your focus, so no matter who you are with, give them your full attention. This one, simple habit will dramatically improve the quality of your time with people and the quality of your relationships.

Find your joy

What activities do you love? What brings you joy? At best, we may be able to enjoy these activities at the weekend; at worst, not at all.

Schedule time in your evenings for the things in your life that bring you joy. Then, when you are involved in this activity, focus on it fully and on nothing else.

Have a balanced dinner

What you eat and when you eat in the evening plays a key role, not only in achieving great sleep, but also your ideal weight and high energy the following day.

Aim to be upright for at least two-to-four hours after eating, before you lie down to sleep. This can be sitting or walking.

In a perfect evening meal, approximately a third of your plate will comprise of a high-protein food such as chicken, fish, tofu or lentils and two-thirds colourful vegetables.

If you are planning a long workout the following morning, you can add a slow-release carbohydrate such as brown rice, quinoa or sweet potato.

Calm your mind and body

To help calm your mind and body from the stimulation of the day, the most effective habit is meditation or deep relaxation. Start with five minutes and build up to 20 minutes.

Here are three simple steps for breathing meditation:

1. Sit cross-legged on the floor with your back supported, or in a chair with your eyes closed.

2. Slowly breathe in through your nose and out through your nose, relaxing as you exhale.

3. Keep your focus and attention on your breathing, and when thoughts come, let them float away like clouds in the sky. Keep your attention focused on your breath: in and out.

Tools to enhance deep relaxation and meditation:

For more information on (TM) Transcendental Meditation (See reading list).

For a great selection of alpha music (a form of music that helps your brain move into the slower more relaxed alpha brain waves) to aid deep relaxation (See reading list).

For some guided meditation download one of the many guided meditation apps (See reading list).

Unplug from technology

Technology is very stimulating for your nervous system and, last thing at night, you don't want to create further stimulation; you want to calm yourself from the stimulation of the day.

We start to produce melatonin when it grows dark. This hormone helps you fall asleep and enhances sleep quality. So, if you're using technology before bed and your house is lit with bright lights, this will interfere with your production of melatonin and affect your sleep.

One of the simplest and most effective habits to develop to help you fall asleep more quickly, and to improve the quality of your sleep, is to avoid all technology one-to-two hours before bed. No TV, laptop, tablet or phone.

In addition, have soft lighting around your home late at night.

Prepare for sleep

I'm often asked what you should do with your last hour before bed if you have turned off all technology.

Here are my top five habits for calming yourself and preparing for sleep during the last hour of the day:

- Have a relaxing chat with your partner.

- Tidy up your home to help create a nice calm and clutter-free environment.

- Have a bath.

- My personal favourite is Yin yoga. This involves calming and relaxing postures that you hold for five minutes per posture.

- Lie in the semi-supine Alexander technique position for around 20 minutes. (See reading list). Both this position and Yin yoga will calm the mind and body as well as relieving the tension from your day. The Alexander technique teaches you to use your body in a more natural, effortless way and helps to improve your posture.

Early to bed

Over the years of coaching people to improve their energy, this one habit has proved to be a key driver in achieving consistently high energy each day. I believe in "early to bed and early to rise". Aim to be in bed by 10.30pm at least four or five nights per week. This will improve the quality of your sleep and ensure you wake up early, giving you time for positive morning habits.

Maintain a relaxed mindset

This final evening habit is particularly important if you have challenges with sleep. Avoid being concerned about sleeping well. Take a relaxed approach towards sleep. The perfect mindset is not to mind how sleep comes, just to be happy to close your eyes for six-to-eight hours each night and relax.

SUMMARY

Take control of your evenings and prioritise the things that bring you joy so your evenings are fulfilling. Put in place the key evening habits to calm yourself from the stimulation of your day so you achieve great sleep and set up your energy for the following day.

MORNING HABITS TO ENERGISE YOUR DAY

INTRODUCTION

Prioritising your evening habits is key. This will enable you to start the day early refreshed and re-energised. This, in turn, sets you up to develop the right morning habits.

Morning habits are not only important for kick-starting your energy, they also set in motion a positive flow for your happiness, creativity and performance for the day.

For me, the first few hours of the morning are by far the most important of the day. If you start out healthy, positive, productive and excited, that's exactly how your day will continue.

THE CHALLENGE

So many of us don't consciously create our ideal morning. For many, the morning just happens in its own haphazard way and we take it as it comes.

But the wrong habits in the morning set in motion a negative chain of events for our mind and body. This, in turn, affects our energy, creativity, productivity and happiness.

THE SOLUTION

As with all the habits in this book, consistency is the golden rule. This is particularly important for your morning habits, so create a strong morning routine that works for you.

Early to rise

The most important morning habit is the time you get up. Make it early and make it consistent. By rising early, you create the time for your positive morning habits and rising at the same time each morning is one of the best habits to help you fall asleep effortlessly each night. Often, the biggest challenge people face with habits in the morning, such as meditation, exercise and breakfast, is making time. This is why it works so well to go to bed early, so you feel comfortable about rising early.

Avoid technology for your first hour

There are a few habits that I swear by and this is one of them. Avoid all technology, in particular your phone, within the first few hours of waking. The start of your day is prime time for positive habits to set you up for the day. Avoiding technology allows you to focus fully on these morning habits.

Introduce morning meditation

Start the day with five minutes of meditation and build up to 20 minutes. Have a chair that allows you to sit upright. As soon as you wake, go to your chair for meditation. A calm and healthy mind is so important and meditation is the best way to deliver that, so prioritise this habit to be your first of the day.

Visualise your goals and your day

Directly after your morning meditation, your mind is in a perfect state for visualising the achievement of your goals. Simply close your eyes and imagine your life with your goals achieved. Visualise achieving your goals with all your senses. The more vividly you can do this, the better. This simple, yet powerful habit need only take two-to-five minutes of your morning. You can use this same approach to visualise your day going exactly the way you want it to.

Practise morning exercise

If your mind is the most important part of you, the second most important element is your body, so prioritise exercise each morning.

The best time to exercise for your energy and for weight loss is during the morning. People who exercise in the morning are also more consistent in their exercise. As the day progresses, things happen and can get in the way of exercising; you are more likely to have an excuse not to exercise if you plan your do it at lunchtime or in the evening. Moving for 20-60 minutes every morning is key. We are all unique, so your activity will depend on your goals and the exercise you enjoy. If you opt for shorter sessions, increase the intensity to achieve maximum benefit. See the exercise habits section for some 20-minute workouts on page 138.

Introduce a high-energy breakfast

I recommend morning exercise on an empty stomach. Then, after you've exercised, it's breakfast time. The secret to a high-energy breakfast is balance. Your balance will be specific to your body and goals. However, as a guide, you should have roughly an even split between the quantity of carbohydrates to protein foods, and ideally include some foods that contain good fats.

1. Include a slow-release carbohydrate to give you sustained energy throughout the morning, such as rye bread, oats, amaranth pops, quinoa flakes, buckwheat flakes or a low-sugar granola.

2. Include a high-protein food; again, this will help give you sustained energy throughout the morning. Try shelled hemp seeds, chia seeds, almond flakes, smoked salmon or eggs.

3. Include a food that is high in good fats; these fats are essential for the body and help to promote overall good health. They can be found in eggs, avocado, seeds or nuts.

SUMMARY

By going to bed earlier and getting up earlier, you achieve better-quality sleep and give yourself time in the morning for the core habits that will help to energise your day. Prioritise your health in the morning and see how this improves your day.

WORK HABITS TO MAXIMISE YOUR CREATIVITY AND PERFORMANCE

INTRODUCTION

Work makes up the majority of our day. We should therefore do our best to make the time at work happy and fulfilling.

Also, ideally, whatever our work, we should perform it to a high level with passion and commitment. If this is achieved, it energises rather than drains us.

THE CHALLENGE

Many people are not happy in their work and the majority are not performing at anywhere near their full potential.

There are many reasons for this. Common reasons include your job not playing to your natural talents and the feeling that there are not enough hours in the day to do all you need to do, which promotes stress. Or maybe you just don't feel passionate about your work or the vision of the organisation doesn't excite you.

THE SOLUTION

The solution is simple to understand, although some work changes can be challenging to put into practice. However given the amount of time we spend at work I truly believe this is a challenge worth accepting.

BELOW ARE SOME OF THE KEY AIMS:

1. Find a job about which you are passionate, or a job where you are passionate about something at work.

2. Consider why your organisation does what it does. Work for an organisation where you really buy into the 'why' of the organisation.

3. If you work for yourself, be clear about why you do what you do. Make sure your 'why' excites and energises you. For example, as I've mentioned, I love helping people to achieve great energy and to be the best they can be, and this is why I do what I do. So each day, when I'm working, I know why my corporate coaching business, EnergiseYou, exists. The reason I wrote this book is to help people to achieve great energy and be the best they can be.

4. Make sure your job plays to your natural talents. This will mean you are able to perform your work to a consistently high standard and your work will energise you naturally. For a great book to help you to discover your strengths, see reading list, on page 183.

5. Work smart using the habits in this chapter. This will allow you to perform better and achieve more in less time with less stress.

Feel a sense of purpose

Understand why your organisation does what it does. Your goal is to work for an organisation (or for yourself) where you are committed to the cause of the organisation and its values. This will give you a sense of purpose and make you feel you are part of something bigger than yourself.

Use your natural talents

Each and every one of us has unique natural talents and when our work allows us to use these each day, we start to develop real strengths.

A strength is created by investing time in your natural talents.

You will know when you are using your natural talents because you will consistently perform your work to a high level. Your work will feel effortless and it will energise you.

Keep your energy positive

This habit seems so obvious as I write it but, like so many of the simple habits, it can be challenging to achieve consistently. Be aware of the energy you put into your work and ensure it is positive energy. This will help you to create your best work.

Prioritise for impact

To have genuine impact at work, you need clarity about the things that affect your success. Take the time now to list the key elements of your job that have the biggest impact on your results.

Once you are clear about these, prioritise them. These areas should be the focus for your week and the top of your daily 'to do' list.

Set work goals

Once you are clear about the elements of your job that have the biggest impact on your results, and you have created a strong habit of prioritising these areas, it is tremendously motivating to set yourself goals. Set a maximum of three goals for the coming three months. Then break down these goals further by setting a maximum of three actions for the coming month; these are the key goals for the month ahead that move you towards your three-month goals.

Schedule your important work

For many roles, it can be highly effective to set specific days and times for particular tasks. For instance, 9am – 10am on a Monday could be set aside for planning your week. Schedule the most important work for the mornings and early part of the week and less important, less challenging work for the late afternoon and the end of your week, when you are less fresh. If you find you have great energy at certain times, schedule the important work for these times.

Note down your ideas

Our brains are not designed to store and retrieve lots of information. It is therefore essential to 'brain dump' good ideas and action points as soon as you think of them, so they don't get lost.

Have a page in your note pad and as soon as you have a great idea or remember a job you need to get done, write it down.

This will mean you can keep your mind clear and forget about these actions until you have time to organise them.

Have a master 'to do' list

Have a master 'to do' list. I suggest, for clarity, writing this on another page in your note pad.

You can refer to your other note pad page, the one you use to 'brain dump' ideas and jobs, and from this list set specific actions on your 'master to do' list.

If your list of actions tends to be fairly long, break your list into sub-headings such as 'health', 'work', 'family' and 'other'.

Prioritise your tasks

You may well label this habit unimportant because it's so simple, but it really is one of the best for productivity.

Create a real focus each day. Start by writing down your three 'must-do' actions for the day (you can also do this the night before if that works for you).

Refer to your master 'to do' list and then decide on the three priority actions for the day. Once you decide these, pick the most important one and focus on that action until it is done. You'll find it satisfying to complete the important tasks and this will help you feel more relaxed and on top of your work as the day progresses.

Do one thing at a time

This is your perfect opportunity to practise the essence of mindfulness at work. Do one thing at a time, with all your focus. Avoid jumping in and out of email. Instead, deal with emails in batches throughout the day. Research shows we are around 44% more productive when we do one thing at a time, compared to swapping between tasks.

Work in intervals

Research shows our brains work best when we work in intervals. Work in 60-90 minute intervals, then take a short break. These intervals do not need to be exact, go with how you feel. Sometimes, an interval could be just 20 minutes and then you'll feel the need for a break. Sometimes, you may be 'in the zone' and feel you can go for two or three hours. The key is to know when you start to experience diminishing returns on your efforts; that's the time to break so you can re-energise.

Re-energise at lunchtime

It's really important to re-energise by working in intervals and taking short breaks. In addition, your lunch break is a great opportunity to switch off and re-energise your mind and body. The three essentials to re-energising at lunchtime are:

1. Take your lunch break away from your computer and get some fresh air and daylight.

2. Avoid your phone to give yourself a full technology break.

3. Eat a lunch containing a high-protein food such as chicken, fish, lentils or tofu and combine with a slow-release carbohydrate food, such as quinoa, brown rice, lots of vegetables or sweet potato. Avoid the high glycaemic index (GI) carbohydrates such as bread, jacket potatoes, crisps and rice cakes.

Set challenging deadlines

A project will expand to fill the time you set aside for it. So, if you say a project will take a month, it will; equally, if you set a one-week deadline, you'll find a way to complete it in a week. Increase productivity by setting a short-focused deadline for each project. You'll be amazed what can be achieved.

Reduce the non-essentials

Make a list of things you do at work that you can either stop doing, delegate or reduce doing. This can help to free up time for the important things. This is a good exercise to do monthly or quarterly.

De-clutter

Being organised at work often means you are just good at juggling tasks. What you'll probably find, however, is that many tasks are unnecessary. As we simplify, we free up space to focus on the important things. Go minimalist: each week or month de-clutter and clear space. Clear emails, clear paperwork, clear documents on your desktop, clear your desk and drawers.

Maintain perfect posture

Given the excessive amount of time we spend sitting at our computers or laptops and, given that we simply weren't designed to sit for long periods of time, it is vital you set up your workstation correctly. Correct set up and posture will keep you as healthy and productive as possible.

If you work in an office, speak to your HR or health and safety department to arrange a workstation assessment. Otherwise, here are the essentials:

1. Sit with your feet flat on the floor, hip-width apart, which allows approximately a 90-degree angle at your knees and hips.

2. Your forearms should be able to rest on the desk with approximately a 90-degree angle at your elbows.

3. Ensure your eye line is level with the top of your computer screen.

4. If you use a laptop, make sure you have a laptop dock. Alternatively, place the laptop on some books to achieve the correct height, and have a separate mouse and keyboard.

Release upper body tension

Even if you have perfect posture at your computer, you will still create tension and blocked energy from sitting in the same position all day. The two most effective ways to relieve the tension and get your energy flowing freely are:

1. Neck, back and shoulder massage. If your company offers energising back massages at work, have one as often as possible.

2. Stretching your neck, back and shoulders daily. Hold each stretch for at least one minute. You'll find some demonstrations of upper body stretches on YouTube.

Manage your email

One of the biggest distractions from doing one thing at a time is email. Manage email traffic by following these five simple rules.

1. Send fewer emails and you'll receive fewer emails.

2. Switch off from work: avoid emails in the evenings and weekends. Also, turn off the auto email 'push' on your smartphone.

3. In order to avoid constant interruptions to your focus, turn off audio alerts on your email and phone.

4. Clear your emails at designated times once or twice a day. Manage your colleagues' expectations so they are clear how often you check your emails. You can check your emails throughout the day so that, if an urgent email comes in,

you can deal with it straight away, but all the others can be cleared together.

5. When you go through your emails, execute one of these six actions on each one:

1) Delete.

2) Respond then delete

3) Forward to someone else then delete.

4) Unsubscribe (if you are on a mailing list that you don't value), then delete.

5) If you don't need to deal with the email immediately, then file it in a follow-up folder, which you can go through and clear once a week.

6) Avoid copying in individuals to your emails unnecessarily.

Manage pressure at work

We all benefit from having some pressure in our lives, it gives us focus and stimulation and, for some, it's essential for motivation. However, the modern lifestyle sometimes puts us under more pressure than we would like, or than is healthy for us. Here is a simple system you can use to manage pressure when it gets too much:

1. Notice the early warning signs. These will tell you when you are under too much pressure; for example, irritability, eating too much or too little, anxiety, sleep problems, forgetfulness.

2. Write down the one, two or three top challenges that are causing you to feel this excess pressure.

3. Write down your ideal solution for each of your challenges.

4. Write down what actions you can take to move from your current situation with these challenges, to your ideal situation.

Here is an example of this process in action:

Challenge
I feel sluggish from sitting at my computer for too long. Every lunchtime or evening I intend to exercise, but something always seems to come up to prevent me going.

Ideal situation
I'm exercising four times a week and my energy feels great.

Actions
Three evenings a week, I'm going to go to bed earlier so I have time for three 20-minute morning weekday workouts. I'm also going to exercise as soon as I get up every Saturday morning for one hour.

Review your performance

Review your work every one-to-three months. To ensure this process is positive, ask yourself these two simple questions.

1. What is going well, what positive things have I achieved?

2. What can I do to improve?

Celebrate your achievements

Some people fail to achieve their goals and become disillusioned. It can also become a pattern to set goals, achieve them, and then focus immediately on the next goal. Give yourself a pat on the back and celebrate your special successes by rewarding yourself with something you love. These could be results you've achieved, challenges you've overcome or improvements you've made.

SUMMARY

We spend so much time at work that it's worth finding a job you love and which plays to your natural talents. At this time it may not be possible to find a job you love, so work on finding the love within your current job. This may be through the relationships you build with your colleagues or through practising mindfulness and gratitude at work.

Once you've found work you love, work smart using the strategies in this section so you can achieve your full potential.

NUTRITION HABITS FOR OPTIMAL HEALTH AND ENERGY

INTRODUCTION

There is no one diet that works for everyone. You are unique, according to many factors such as your age, gender, size, activity level, food likes and dislikes, food intolerances, health goals and preferences (for example, vegetarian or vegan).

So, rule number one is to find the way of eating the right foods that works for you. This section will show you how to practise mindfulness in your eating habits for health and energy.

THE CHALLENGE

So much of what we consume does not serve our health and energy. We are highly influenced by the marketing efforts of food and drink companies and by the urge to consume addictive substances such as sugar, salt, bad fats, caffeine and alcohol.

THE SOLUTION

The solution is mindful eating, which I will explain in this section. All the most advanced nutrition principles are simple. The challenge lies in making habit changes, and the key is to listen to your body and be mindful of the foods and drinks you consume. In this way, you will naturally create a nutrition plan for yourself that serves your unique situation.

As you will see, this section contains a lot of habits and it can be easy to feel overwhelmed by so many changes. Remember, you only need to pick the three habit changes that you feel will be the most suitable and achievable for you right now. In addition, I want to remind you of the importance of the 80/20 rule with nutrition. One of the biggest mistakes I see people make with healthy eating, is swinging between a strict, restrictive diet and losing the plot, eating everything in sight.

See this as your journey to making small achievable habit changes over time, as opposed to extreme changes that last a couple of weeks.

Practise mindful eating

Here are some useful tips for mindful eating:

- Have you full attention on your food, remove distractions such as the TV or your phone.

- Appreciate the colours and smells of your food.

- Bring your full awareness to how the food tastes.

- Eat at half your normal pace and take small bites.

- Stop halfway through your meal and take a break to notice how full you feel.

- Avoid talking while eating; if you need to talk, take a break from eating.

- Become aware of your need for the food you have in front

of you. This can help you to control portion size and can help you manage temptation for desserts.

Minimise these foods and drinks

There are many foods and drinks that simply don't serve you, especially if you consume them on a regular basis. The golden rule with food is to aim for whole foods. Heavily processed foods and drinks are best cut from your diet completely or kept to a minimum. With some of these foods and drinks, you can apply the 80/20 rule and have them occasionally. Here ' are the main foods and drinks to cut out or minimise:

- Foods high in refined sugar

- Processed foods

- Foods containing wheat and gluten

- Dairy products

- Fried foods

- Foods to which you are intolerant and that don't make you feel good – in other words those that create bloating, tiredness, skin problems, headaches. If you'd like to find out the foods to which you're intolerant. (See reading list for the test I recommend).

- Red meat

- Fizzy, sugary drinks including diet drinks

- Caffeine

- Alcohol

Indulge occasionally

We all have certain foods and drinks that we love. The great thing about having these foods or drinks sometimes is that our pleasure and appreciation for these increases. For example, a morning coffee a couple of times a week will taste so much better than drinking coffee three or four times a day. What foods and drinks do you love that you can have sometimes, to really savour the experience?

Include these foods and drinks

As a rule, whole foods are best. You are eating foods in their natural state such as meat, fish, fruit, vegetables, seeds, nuts and quinoa.

These foods and drinks are nutritionally rich. Aim to fill as much of your diet with them as possible:

- Seasonal fruit and vegetables

- Quinoa

- Amaranth

- Buckwheat

- Millet

- Lentils

- Sweet potatoes

- Fresh fish

- Organic turkey or chicken

- Sprouted beans

- Chickpeas

- Hemp seeds

- Chia seeds

- Pumpkin seeds

- Almonds

- Brazil nuts

- Bee pollen

- Spirulina

- Maca

- Goji berries

- Blueberries

- Cacao

- Dried coconut

- Hemp, pumpkin, flax and coconut oil

- Dates

- Almond butter

- Matcha tea

- Coconut water

- Almond milk

- Pumpkin seed milk

Go organic where possible

Choose organic options as often as possible. These foods contain fewer chemicals, which in the long term means a healthier you.

Here are the most important foods to buy organic, as the non-organic options are heavily sprayed with chemicals. The foods listed in the previous 'maximise' habit and the organic foods below can be more expensive, but to balance it out, I recommend cutting back on alcohol, coffee, fizzy drinks and meat, and spending the money you save on nutritionally rich foods .

- Strawberries

- Blueberries

- Apples

- Nectarines

- Peaches

- Cucumbers

- Kale

- Spinach

- Avocados

- Oats

- Quinoa

- All soya products, such as soya milk, tofu, edamame

- Chicken

- Turkey

Make healthy swaps

One of the simplest ways to improve your nutrition habits is to swap unhealthy foods and drinks for healthier options. The following is a list of some simple swaps for breakfast, lunch, dinner, snacks and desserts.

BREAKFAST

Swap toast and refined breakfast cereals high in sugar (true for the majority of brands) with milk for:

- Eggs on rye bread

- Amaranth pops or porridge oats with seeds and berries with almond milk

- Fruit or vegetable smoothie with blended seeds

SNACKS

Swap refined foods such as biscuits, crisps, rice cakes, and cheap chocolate for:

- Fresh fruit and nuts

- Oatcakes with almond butter

- Coconut yogurt with blueberries and seeds on top

- Super food energy balls. Ideally make your own using the recipes on page 116 and 117. Alternatively, TREK whole food energy bars or peanut Bounce protein balls are the next best thing. Many of these bars contain sugar so have occasionally

- Hummus, strips of chicken with cucumber and carrots

LUNCH

Swap sandwiches and crisps for:

- Chicken, quinoa and avocado salad

- Vegetable soup with a healthy protein food such as chicken, fish, tofu, lentils or quinoa

- Any salad with a healthy protein food such as chicken, fish, tofu, lentils or quinoa

- Sardines and avocado on rye bread

DINNER

Swap heavy, starchy carbohydrate meal, e.g. pasta, rice, potatoes, noodles, bread, for:

- Lots of colourful vegetables with a healthy protein food such as chicken, fish, tofu, lentils or quinoa

- Salmon and vegetables

- Rosemary chicken, olive oil and vegetables

- Honey, mustard and soya sauce tofu kebabs with vegetables

DESSERTS

Swap desserts high in wheat, dairy and refined sugar for:

- Coconut yogurt, strawberries and crushed almonds

- Apple crumble, using oats and crushed almonds for the crumble

- Homemade superfood energy balls, see page 116 and 117

- Blueberries, crushed dark chocolate and cashew nuts

Reduce meat consumption

There is no single way of eating that works for everyone. You have to find what works for your personal circumstances. Part of mindfulness is becoming more aware of making decisions that serve you. You can further extend this philosophy to being more aware of the decisions you make for the health and happiness of animals and our planet.

Now, I'm not about to preach that you have to be vegan or vegetarian; however, I am going to suggest that you make a small habit change to reduce the meat and fish you consume. There are three big benefits to this:

1. If you eat less meat, you will be able to eat better-quality meat when you do have it.

2. One of the biggest causes of global warming is the meat industry. The more animals we breed for food, the more we increase greenhouse gas emissions, carbon dioxide and methane. By reducing the meat you eat, in particular red meat, you are helping our planet.

3. There is no getting away from the fact that because we eat so much meat and fish, the way in which we mass breed and kill animals, means they do not enjoy happy or healthy lives.

Here are some examples of small habit changes you could make. Choose one you feel works for you:

Either cut out red meat from your diet or reduce it to once a week or fortnight, or even once a month.

When you eat chicken or turkey, choose organic, free range.

Eat meat or fish once a day, or every other day, and introduce high-protein alternatives into your diet such as tofu, lentils, beans, quinoa, seeds and nuts. Set aside one or two days a week during which you only eat vegetarian meals.

Introduce nut or seed milk

Most people stop breastfeeding up to two years after birth, but many continue drinking cow's milk for the rest of their lives. I recommend switching from cows' milk to nut or seed milk. It's much healthier and will benefit animals and the planet. If you buy nut or seed milk in a health food shop, go for the version without added sugar.

If you prefer to make your own (which is far cheaper and healthier) simply blend one cup of seeds or nuts with three or four cups of water. If you wish, you can strain away the pulp after blending, but personally I leave it all in. It also helps to soak your seeds or nuts overnight in water before blending. My personal favourites are almond milk and pumpkin seed milk. If you want to add some sweetness to the milk, include one or two pitted dates when you blend.

Reduce your sugar intake

Sugar is one of the biggest problems in the modern diet. Many years ago, sugar was something we consumed occasionally;

now it's added to most processed foods, and nearly all drinks contain sugar. Add to this the explosion of the ready-made fruit juice market and we are simply consuming too much sugar.

Here are some simple sugar habits to help you reduce the sugar in your diet:

- Minimise foods with more than 5g of added sugar per 100g, or avoid all added sugar.

- Minimise all drinks and yogurts that contain sugar.

- Avoid adding sugar to anything you eat or drink.

- Read food ingredients, watching out for foods where sugar is first, second or third on the ingredients list.

- Watch out for 'low fat' foods as these often contain sugar.

- Look out for sugar described as syrup, sucrose or honey on the list of ingredients.

- Aim to eat two pieces of fruit in the morning and combine these with seeds or nuts to slow down the sugar release.

- Note that fruit is better than fruit juice as the fibre helps to slow down the sugar release.

- Aim for foods and drinks that have a sweet taste naturally, such as root vegetables, herbal teas and nuts.

- When eating chocolate, opt for at least 80% dark chocolate

- Know that the more sweetness you consume, the more you will crave.

- Look out for foods that have 'sugar-free' labels but which still contain processed, concentrated natural sugars or artificial sweeteners.

- Sleep well. We are more prone to sugar cravings after a poor night's sleep.

- Take regular exercise – it helps to burn the sugar and encourages you make healthier food choices.

- Practise mindfulness. This will ensure you are present and helps you make decisions that serve you, as opposed to operating on autopilot.

Make your own healthy snacks

I'm a big fan of homemade superfood energy balls for snacks. These are not only much healthier and less expensive than anything you can buy, but I believe they also taste better.

Here are my top three favourite superfood energy ball recipes.

Note: each recipe makes around 14 balls. Simply mix all the ingredients into a large bowl and then bind the mixture together with your hands, making 14 balls, just slightly bigger than a golf ball.

SUPERFOOD ENERGY BALLS WITH ALMOND BUTTER

100g of shelled hemp seeds
100g of chia seeds
75g of cacao power
50g of maca powder
150g of pitted dates (blend in a food processor)
25g of Goji berries
1x 170g jar of almond butter

SUPERFOOD ENERGY BALLS WITH HAZELNUT BUTTER

100g of almonds (buy in powder form or blend in a food processor)
50g of chia seeds
50g of hazelnuts (blend roughly in a food processor)
75g of cacao power
25g of bee pollen
150g of pitted dates (blend in a food processor)
1x 170g jar of hazelnut butter

SUPER FOOD ENERGY BALLS WITH CASHEW BUTTER

100g of shelled hemp seeds
100g of pumpkin seeds (blend in a food processor)
75g of cacao power
50g of maca powder
Grated orange peel from one orange
150g of pitted dates (blend in a food processor)
1x 170g jar of cashew nut butter

Understand food labels

Learning to read food labels will ensure you are mindful of the food and drink you consume.

Here are a few elements to look out for on food labels:

- How many grams of fat, carbohydrates, which are made up of sugars and salt, does the food contain per 100g?

- Fat – avoid food with more than 6g of saturated fat per 100g and all trans fats and hydrogenated fats.

- Carbohydrates which are sugars; keep foods that contain more than 5g of sugar per 100g to a minimum.

- Salt – choose foods that have less than 1g of salt per 100g.

Balance carbohydrates, protein and fats

Being mindful of the balance of carbohydrate, protein and fat in your diet is key for health and energy.

Everyone's needs are different, according to body type and goals, but as a general rule for good health, energy and weight management, aim for around 40% to 50% of your daily calories to come from good, slow-release carbohydrates, 30%–35% from good protein and 20%–30% from good fats.

A simple way to work this out is to make each meal and snack just over half good carbohydrates, just under half good protein and ideally include a small amount of good fats.

Be mindful that one gram of fat contains nine calories, whereas one gram of carbohydrate or one gram of protein contains four calories. This is obviously key when balancing the different food groups.

Learning to read food labels and having a general understanding of the carbohydrate, protein and fat makeup of each food, will help to ensure you have a good balance.

Healthy carbohydrates – aim to get the majority of your carbohydrates from these sources:
Fruit, vegetables, quinoa, amaranth, buckwheat, oatcakes, brown rice, basmati rice, no added sugar granola cereal, porridge oats, soya beans, kidney beans, butter beans, lentils, pulses, chickpeas, pinto beans, sweet potatoes.

Less-good carbohydrates – aim to keep to a minimum:
Biscuits, crisps, refined cereals, chips, chocolate, sweets, bread, rice cakes, croissants, waffles, potatoes, pasta, noodles, white rice, fizzy drinks and drinks high in sugar.

Healthy protein – aim to get the majority of your protein from these sources:
Chicken, turkey, fish, nuts and seeds, tofu, lentils, beans, sprouting beans or lentils, mung dal, eggs, quinoa, amaranth, purple-sprouting broccoli.

Less-good protein – aim to keep to a minimum, as these foods are high in the bad fats:
Red meat and cheese.
Healthy fats – aim to get the majority of your fat from these sources:
Fish, nuts, seeds, olive oil, flaxseed oil, sesame oil, coconut oil, avocados, nut butter, coconut yogurt.

Less-good fats - aim to keep to a minimum:
Red meat, cheese, biscuits, crisps, chocolate, croissants, chips, fried foods.

Introduce fasting

This is not for everyone, but research shows there are many great benefits to your health, energy, digestion and weight loss when you use some kind of fasting system. There is also evidence that fasting can help to slow the ageing process, as well as reducing the chance of disease.

There are many ways in which you can fast. I have tested them all and found the system below to be the easiest and the one that delivers the best results for my energy and body shape.

I would only recommend introducing this into your life once you have created a healthy, balanced diet of nutritionally rich whole foods.

Note: Consult your doctor or a nutritionist before introducing a fasting system into your diet and avoid this form of fasting if you are pregnant or diabetic.

Here are your simple guidelines for fasting:

- Eat your last meal of the day at 6pm or 7pm at latest.

- Then fast for 16 hours every day, i.e. if you finished eating your evening meal at 6pm, you would eat your breakfast at 10am.

From when you wake to 10am aim to drink 1.5 litres of water. This may include herbal teas.

To maximise your fat-loss results from this system, exercise in the morning, before breakfast, and leave at least an hour after you finish exercising before you eat.

- Your meal times would be roughly as follows:

  Breakfast: 10am – 11am
  Lunch: 2pm
  Dinner: 6pm-7pm

- If you feel the need to introduce a snack late morning or early afternoon you can do this.

- Unlike The Fast Diet (5:2)™, where you reduce your calories for two days per week, with this form of fasting you fast every day, giving your body a daily 16-hour fast. Your initial couple of weeks may be challenging until your hunger hormones adjust to the new timings, but after that it's effortless, especially as a large part of the fasting period is while you are asleep.

- Sometimes, it's good to fast for a little longer, for example, 16-20 hours' fasting. The more you are in tune with your body, the more you will feel what is right for you.

Set timings for your food and drink

If you introduce the fasting system, this will give you your timings for eating. That aside, there are some key principles of which to be mindful:

- Drink at least one litre of water within your first two-to-three hours of waking.

- Aim for at least three hours between each meal to allow for full digestion.

- To aid digestion, aim for at least two-to-four hours of being upright after your evening meal before sleep.

- Avoid drinking lots of liquid while eating, or within an hour of eating, as this will affect your digestion.

- Avoid strenuous exercise within two hours of eating.

Manage your portion size

Portion size is a key driver for achieving a healthy weight. Your portion size will be driven by your weight goal.

The key principle, if you are trying to lose weight, is that you need to create a daily calorie deficit. Aim for approximately 300 calories less per day than your normal daily calorie requirement. Equally, aim for about 300 calories more than your daily requirement if you are aiming to put on weight.

In saying that, I advise against calorie counting for two reasons: first, it becomes all-consuming and second, not all calories are the same, so this can be confusing. Instead, use a trial-and-error system with your portion sizes until you feel your portion sizes are correct for the goals you've set.

Here are some simple principles to follow:

- Ideally make lunch your biggest meal of the day.

- Make breakfast and dinner roughly the same size.

- Keep sugar and complex carbohydrates to a minimum in the evening. If you do eat them, keep the portion size small and choose quinoa, sweet potatoes or brown rice rather than bread, pasta, rice or noodles.

- A couple of whole pieces of fruit a day are good to eat before 12 noon. This will give your body time to burn the sugar through the afternoon.

- Foods high in good fats are great. However, they are also high in calories, so aim for smaller portions; for example, two dessert spoons of seeds per day, 15 nuts per day, half an avocado per day.

Achieve great digestion

Healthy digestion is key to overall health and energy.

Here are some simple principles to help you achieve healthy digestion:

- Eat slowly, chew your food well, and avoid eating on the move or when you are stressed or upset.

- Mindful eating means doing one thing at a time with all your focus on your food. Avoid eating while reading, watching TV or in front of your computer.

- Eat breakfast, lunch and dinner at roughly the same times each day.

- Eat until you are no more than 70% full, i.e. avoid feeling completely full after eating.

- Avoid drinking lots of water or other liquids with your meal. A glass of water is fine but too much will affect your digestion.

- Make sure your evening meal is light and give yourself at least two-to-four hours between your meal and bedtime.

- Eat a healthy, balanced diet by following the nutrition habits in this chapter.

Detox when needed

There are certain foods and drinks that it is advisable either to cut out or cut down. The extent to which you minimise these will determine your need to detox from these foods and drinks. Of course, if you never eat or drink any of these foods, a detox is unnecessary.

If you have some of these in your diet, I would recommend a detox once every three-to-six months. It's excellent for improving your energy, your immune system and skin, while cleansing yourself of the build-up of toxins and waste. This would ideally be for a month, but if that sounds too difficult, start with a fortnight or even a week.

Your detox week or month has three simple elements:

1. Ensure you drink at least two litres of water per day.

2. Fill your diet with nutritionally rich foods. See the 'maximise' habit for a list of foods.

3. Cut out the foods and drinks listed below (if this seems too

challenging, cut as many as you can. Then on your next detox, aim to cut more):

- Wheat and gluten products

- Dairy products

- Foods high in refined sugar

- Processed foods

- Deep-fried foods

- Foods that don't make you feel good, causing bloating, tiredness, skin problems or headaches

- Red meat

- Caffeine

- Alcohol

- Fizzy, sugary drinks

Increase alkaline foods and drinks

A typical diet tends to be highly acid forming; acid-forming foods include fruit, meat, fish, bread, pasta and processed foods. Increasing alkaline-forming foods and drinks in your diet keeps you in balance and has big benefits for your health and energy. Here are three of the best habits to commit to:

- Eat green vegetables at lunch and dinner as often as possible.

- Eat almonds daily. These are the only alkaline nut: 10 to 15 nuts is a good quantity as a snack, or opt for almond milk.

- Drink alkaline water. You will need to buy an alkaline water filter or use alkaline drops. You can find these online.

Keep hydrated

There are many factors that affect how much liquid you need each day. Two litres of liquid per day is a good guide and this can include herbal teas.

There are some factors that would suggest a higher intake, for example, if you're bigger than average in height and weight; it's a hot day; you've exercised; you work in a building with air conditioning or central heating; you've drunk alcohol.

Aim for the majority of your liquid to come in the form of mineral or filtered water and herbal tea. To help achieve this, buy a one-litre BPA free water bottle, fill it at the start of the day and drink it all by around 5pm.

Keep caffeinated drinks to a maximum of two per day. Matcha tea is the best option. This is a form of green tea that is higher in antioxidants than regular green tea.

If you've tried juicing, listen to your body. Some body types do not cope well with fresh juices, mine included. If you do feel ok, go for freshly made juice, leave the pulp in the drink and consume directly after juicing.

Keep alcohol to a minimum. If you drink for the pleasure of the taste, for example, wine, I would recommend that you have no more than one or two glasses two-to-three evenings per week.

Take three supplements

There are some people who will say you don't need any supplements as you get everything you need from your diet. From my experience, not to mention the detailed research I have done in this area, I find this not to be the case.

Our diets, the quality of the foods we eat, and the pressures on our bodies, mean we rarely get enough vitamins, minerals and Omega 3 fats.

There are three daily supplements from which most people can benefit:

1. A good multivitamin each morning: excellent for overall health and a strong immune system. The brand Solar VM 2000 is a good option.

2. A high-quality Omega 3 each morning: excellent for a healthy heart, circulation, joints and skin. The brand Eskimo 3 to be a good option.

3. Vitamin C (1,000mg) each morning: excellent for overall health and a strong immune system. I recommend the brand Biocare Vit C 1000.

Shop for healthy foods

You will eat what's in your home. One of the simplest ways to stop eating nutritionally poor foods and to create a diet of nutritionally rich foods is to ensure you only shop for the right foods and drinks.

Many of the nutritionally rich foods, such as seeds, nuts, quinoa, cacao powder, maca powder and bee pollen, to name a few, are much cheaper to buy online than from a health food shop.

Prepare your lunch for work

Prepare your lunch the night before to take to work the next day. This habit may well not appeal to you; however, for some people, it is essential. Here are three examples of people who really benefit from this habit:

- Individuals who have a huge workload and are so busy with deadlines and meetings that they find it hard to leave work and grab a healthy lunch.

- People who are on the road a great deal, such as field sales staff. These individuals may have time to eat lunch but too often resort to buying a pie or sandwich in a petrol station – neither of which I'd recommend.

- People who work at a location where there are no healthy options for lunch.

SUMMARY

There are many components to advanced nutrition. As with all your decisions, the key is to make these your new habits so you can benefit from optimum health and energy.

Select three nutrition habit changes that you feel are best for you right now and really give them your focus for the next month.

EXERCISE HABITS TO TRANSFORM YOUR BODY

INTRODUCTION

Like nutrition, there is no single magic way to exercise that works for everyone. However, the bottom line is that we all need regular daily exercise. The modern lifestyle is extremely sedentary, so we need to embed exercise into our daily routine just like brushing our teeth.

THE CHALLENGE

There are two major challenges that most people face with exercise: achieving consistency and getting the results they desire from the exercise they do.

THE SOLUTION

In this section, I will cover the habits that will ensure that you are consistent with your exercise and that will help you to achieve maximum benefit from whichever exercise regime you choose.

Be consistent with your exercise

The golden rule with exercise is consistency. Here are the three key elements to help ensure you're consistent:

1. **Find exercise you enjoy.**
   If you feel you don't really enjoy any exercise then find the exercise you like the most (or hate least!) and keep focused on the benefits for your mind and body. By focusing on the benefits of regular exercise, you will start to change how you feel about it.

2. **Find exercise that fits in with your lifestyle.**
   The key here is to ensure that whatever exercise you do, you practise it at a time of day, and a location, that is convenient to you.

3. **Exercise in the morning as often as possible.**
   Research shows that morning exercisers are considerably more consistent with their exercise than those who exercise at lunchtime or evenings. So, if possible, schedule your exercise for the morning, even if this is only one or two sessions per week.

Keep focused on your exercise

Exercise is a perfect opportunity for practising doing one thing at a time with all your focus.

Either don't take your phone with you when you exercise, or if you need your phone for music during exercise, switch it to 'plane mode'.

Then, whatever exercise you are doing, focus. Where you focus will depend on the type of exercise you are doing.

Here are a few examples:

- If you are running, focus on the rhythm of your breathing and focus on keeping your core stomach muscles contracted.

- If you are playing tennis, focus on the tennis ball and nothing else.

- If you are doing a resistance-training workout, focus on the muscles you are working on at the time.

- If you are practising yoga, focus on your breath.

Include the three exercise types

There are three main types of exercise. Aim to include all three in your exercise programme for overall fitness, toning, body shape and posture:

Cardiovascular. This includes any exercise that keeps your heart rate high, such as:

a) Cardio-based exercise classes such as zumba, body attack, kick-boxing and aerobics.

b) A cardio-based exercise DVD.

c) Sports that involve cardio such as cycling, swimming, skipping, running, football, netball and power-walking.

d) A cardio-based fitness programme that you can follow at home. (Ask a fitness professional to write one for you, or look up a programme online).

e) A military fitness class or other outdoor boot-camp circuit class.

f) A cardio-based programme at the gym, set by a
    fitness professional.

Resistance training. This includes using weights as your
resistance either with machines, free weights, bands or your
own body weight:

a) Take a resistance-based exercise class such as
    body pump.

b) Ask a fitness professional to write you a home-based
    resistance programme or look one up online.

c) Take part in a military fitness class or an outdoor boot
    camp circuit class that involves resistance work.

d) Follow a resistance-based exercise DVD.

e) Use resistance bands (when you buy them, they come with
    examples of exercises).

f) Join a gym and follow a resistance programme from
    a fitness professional.

Stretching. This may include:

a) Joining a yoga or Pilates class, or doing personal yoga
    or Pilates sessions at home.

b) A stretching exercise DVD or Wii Fit, or following a yoga
    book/DVD.

c) Searching online (there are hundreds of stretching videos to choose from).

d) Asking a personal trainer or yoga instructor to write you a home-based stretching programme.

The three key drivers for the type of exercise to choose are:

1. Do exercise you enjoy.

2. Do exercise that fits in with your lifestyle.

3. Do exercise that helps you achieve your health goals. If you are unsure which type of exercise will help you to achieve your goals, consult a fitness professional.

Set a goal for your exercise frequency

How often should you exercise? The answer to this depends on many factors such as your fitness level, the amount of time you can dedicate to exercise, your health goals and your age.

There are, however, a few key points to help convince you to exercise more:

With the increased use of technology, the modern lifestyle is extremely sedentary. Therefore, even if you achieve one hour of exercise every day, this is still just one hour of movement out of 24 hours.

If you exercise five, six or seven times a week, make sure

you create variety in your exercise plan as this will help your energy and overall fitness balance.

Regardless of the time you set aside for exercise aim to be more active generally:

• Walk to your destination whenever possible.

• Always take the stairs and always walk up escalators.

• Always do something active at the weekend.

• Take regular breaks from your computer and always take your lunch break away from your desk.

Be smart with your intensity

There are three main intensity types:

1) Your comfort zone. Most people in a gym exercise in this zone with little benefit as they are just going through the motions, doing the same exercise without really pushing themselves. Having said that, some days your energy will feel low, and on these days, exercising within your comfort zone can be perfect.

2) Your pain zone. This means you are pushing yourself too hard. If you are a high-performing athlete then this is needed. However, for the average person, the two key problems with this zone are that it can lead to injury and it usually means a long recovery period as your body will feel extremely sore for up to seven days afterwards.

3) Your discomfort zone. This is your ideal zone that challenges you and stresses the body just enough to make improvements, without creating excessive muscular soreness.

Vary your exercise

There are many ways to vary your exercise, including the type of exercise you undertake, the length of time you exercise and the level of intensity.

There are two key elements to consider with your variation:

1. Variation through your week: vary either the type, time, or intensity of each workout.

2. Vary your overall programme every six weeks. This is key to maintaining the benefits of exercise, as your body will adapt after six weeks and therefore not gain as much benefit continuing the same routine.

Keep improving your technique

Whatever exercise you engage in, do it correctly. If you are unsure of the perfect technique and alignment, consult an expert. Whether you do yoga, exercises in the gym or play a sport, keep working on your technique. As with your overall health, energy and happiness you can always improve on your technique and you will get more out of exercise and enjoy it more.

Stay relaxed

Whatever exercise you focus on, relax your body. This applies to all exercise. When playing tennis keep your arm relaxed as you swing, when cycling, keep you upper body relaxed, and, when running, keep your upper body and face relaxed. This will maximise your efficiency.

There are a few exceptions to this; for example, when doing resistance training you will be contracting and tightening the muscles you are working, but make sure the rest of your body is relaxed.

There are also some exercises that benefit from keeping your core stomach muscles contracted for overall stability, such as running and resistance training.

Listen to your body

Listen to your body every time you exercise. Adapt the time, type and intensity of your exercise to the way you are feeling that day.

The more you listen to your body and give it what it needs each day, the greater the benefits.

Note: this is not to be confused with giving up too early. Sometimes you may feel like a short, low-intensity workout when, in fact, if you push yourself, you will feel energised to do more. This is all part of being in tune with what your body needs each day.

Avoid exercises that don't work for your body type

We were not all created the same. This means that there will be certain exercises and sports that are best to avoid. This is key to avoiding injury, while achieving the maximum benefit from exercise.

So how do you know what exercise to avoid? Start by listening to your body when you do certain exercises. Below are some examples of what I avoid and why. Remember this is unique to each person.

- Long-distance running or any endurance cardio. My body is more designed for interval-training cardio and fast sprinting.

- I avoid all yoga apart from Yin yoga. I find the slow, relaxed stretching in Yin is far more effective for my body and I can get in tune with my breath more easily.

- Squats and deadlifts in the gym using heavy weights. Even with perfect technique, my lower back screams "no!" to these exercises.

In a nutshell, listen to your own body and give it what it loves and what naturally works for your body type. Avoid the exercises and sports that don't work for your body.

This can take some time, you will discover certain exercises may be hard when you first start, but then they become natural. The exercises that don't fit your body type will never become natural, even with lots of practice.

Introduce 20-minute morning workouts

With morning exercise, you will benefit from energy and calorie burning all day. If you can't make the morning, the next best time would be around the middle of the day. But do your best to achieve at least one or two morning workouts per week.

The challenge for many can be finding time in the morning for exercise.

The two solutions to this are:

1. Ensure you go to bed early and rise early to give you time for morning exercise.

2. If you are really short of time, go for a high-intensity 20-minute workout.

Here are some examples:

NOTE: Consult an exercise or health professional before you start any exercise programme, always listen to your body, and adjust your intensity accordingly. If you are just starting an exercise programme go for short, low-intensity workouts for your first two-to-four weeks to allow your body to adjust to regular exercise in a gradual way.

If you are unsure of the correct technique for any of these exercises consult a fitness professional. You can also find demonstrations of each exercise on YouTube.

INTENSE CARDIO WORKOUT

- 20-minute run or cycle as fast as you can manage

INTERVAL TRAINING WORKOUT

- Interval training for 20 minutes, running, cycling or using any cardio machine

- Do one minute fast, then one minute medium/slow. Alternate for 20 minutes

HIGH-INTENSITY INTERVAL-TRAINING WORKOUT

- High-intensity running, cycling or on any cardio machine for 20 minutes

- Do 20 seconds as hard as you can, then 60-90 seconds slow. Alternate for 20 minutes

LEGS, CHEST AND ABS CIRCUIT

Complete this circuit non-stop five times:

- 20 squats

- 20 press-ups (have your knees on the floor if you need to)

- 20 abdominal crunches

LEGS, ARMS AND ABS CIRCUIT

Complete this circuit non-stop four to five times:

- 20 lunges, alternate leg

- 15 tricep dips (use a bench or a heavy chair that won't fall back)

- 15 bicep curls with weights or a rubber band/tube

- 20 abdominal crunches

LEGS, BACK AND ABS CIRCUIT

Complete this circuit non-stop four-to-five times:

- 20 squats, super slow

- 20 bent over row with weights or a rubber band/tube

- 20 lunges on alternate leg

- 20 abdominal side twists

CHEST, BACK, SHOULDERS AND ABS CIRCUIT

Complete this circuit non-stop four times:

- 20 press-ups (have your knees on the floor if you need to)

- 20 abdominal crunches

- 20 bent over row with weights or a rubber band/tube

- 15 upright row with weights or a rubber band/tube

- 15 shoulder presses with weights or a rubber band/tube

LEGS, CARDIO AND ABS CIRCUIT

Complete this circuit non-stop four-to-five times:

- 20 squats, super slow and low

- Skipping rope with the heels coming up to your bum for 30 to 60 seconds

- 20 lunges alternate leg

- 20 abdominal crunches

CHEST, SHOULDERS AND ABS CIRCUIT

Complete this circuit non-stop four-to-five times:

- 20 super slow press ups (have your knees on the floor if you need to)

- 30 seconds plank position

- 30 seconds 'downward dog' yoga position

- 20 abdominal crunches

SUMMARY

Build exercise into your weekly routine. Find exercise you love (or tolerate!) and that fits your lifestyle. For maximum benefits, exercise in the morning.

Learn to be in tune with your body and give it the type, time and intensity of exercise it needs on a daily basis.

RELAXATION HABITS FOR YOUR MIND AND BODY

INTRODUCTION

The modern lifestyle means a daily relaxation habit is no longer a luxury but an essential component for a healthy mind and body, and a key driver for achieving health, energy and quality sleep.

THE CHALLENGE

There are four main reasons why we need a daily relaxation habit:

1. The quantity of time we spend with technology, such as computers, laptops, tablets, smart phones and television every day. This high exposure is extremely stimulating to our nervous system, which leads to low energy, burn out, mental fatigue and sleep problems.

2. The sheer volume of activity that we cram into our lives and the speed with which we rush through it. Again, this has a stimulating effect on our nervous systems.

3. City life and the stress of commuting has a stimulating effect on the nervous system. In contrast, nature such as the sea, countryside or mountains has a calming effect.

4. Many people add to the above with stimulants such as caffeine, sugar, alcohol, cigarettes, energy drinks and recreational drugs.

THE SOLUTION

The challenge is that much of the aforementioned (particularly 1, 2 and 3) is part of how we live.

However, you can make some adjustments by reducing your technology use, simplifying your life, slowing down occasionally, getting out into the nature as often as possible and minimising the stimulants in your life.

Even if you manage to make the changes I've mentioned, a daily relaxation habit is a great way to calm your mind, body and nervous system from the stimulation of the modern way of living.

Introduce a daily relaxation habit

As with exercise, it's important to find a daily relaxation habit that you enjoy and that fits with your lifestyle. That said, in my experience, meditation is by far the most effective way to calm your mind, body and nervous system.

Here are some examples of daily relaxation habits:

• My personal favourite. Transcendental meditation (TM). (For more information see reading list)

• Any form of meditation that you find effortless. This could include using one of the many meditation apps. (for more information see reading list)

• Sitting in silence with your eyes closed.

- Sitting listening to relaxing music with your eyes closed.

- Having a bath with scented candles.

- Going for a walk in a park, forest, mountains or by the sea.

When to schedule your relaxation habit

There are three highly beneficial times for your daily relaxation habit:

1. As soon as you get out of bed. For example, I start my day with 20 minutes of TM meditation as soon as I wake up. Because you relax so deeply during TM meditation, this is like 20 minutes of extra quality sleep, you are not missing out on any sleep.

   The other benefit of enjoying your relaxation habit as soon as you wake is that you are prioritising this habit ahead of anything else in your day. TM meditation is one of the best habits for my health, energy and happiness, so it comes first in my day.

2. As soon as you get home from work, or if you are able to get a seat on the bus or train journey home, meditate. This will help to create a partition between work and free time and will re-energise you so you can enjoy your evening with greater energy.

3. During your last hour or two before bed. As I mentioned in the evening habits section, turn off all technology an hour or two before bed. This will give you plenty of time for your evening relaxation habit.

You will also be clearing out the stresses of the day and calming your nervous system from all the stimulation. This will dramatically improve the quality of your sleep.

Duration of your relaxation

The relaxation habit you choose will determine how much time you spend on it. For example, it could be a 20-minute meditation or a 45-minute walk in nature. The two key elements are:

1. Prioritise a relaxation habit and make sure you practise it every day.

2. Make sure you spend enough time focusing on your habit to ensure you really do relax your mind, body and nervous system. The more in tune with your body you become, the more you will recognise how long you need each day to relax fully.

Relax your body fully

To ensure you go into deep relaxation, it is important to relax your body fully, removing all the tension you are holding.

If you meditate, it is always best to be seated or cross-legged with your back supported. Personally, I prefer to sit upright in a chair so I am fully relaxed while meditating. If you go for a country walk or have a relaxing bath, bring your awareness to each part of your body and relax.

Remove distractions

Removing all distractions is vital for relaxation. The biggest distraction is your phone. So whether you meditate, go for a walk or have a bath, turn off your phone so you can truly relax. Remember that technology is highly stimulating for your nervous system, so you won't fully relax with a phone in your pocket. Even if it is turned off, you'll be tempted to turn it back on again.

SUMMARY

In the same way that you need a daily exercise habit to counter the sedentary 21st century lifestyle, and to maintain a healthy mind and body, you also need a daily relaxation habit to calm your mind, body and nervous system. As with your exercise habit, the key is to make your daily relaxation habit consistent.

Some of the biggest improvements I've seen in people's energy and happiness has come from simply introducing a daily relaxation habit. It's a small commitment that reaps a very big reward.

PEOPLE HABITS FOR MORE POSITIVE RELATIONSHIPS

INTRODUCTION

This is often an area of our lives we may not associate with our health and energy. However, how we interact with those around us not only plays a key role in our happiness, but has also been proven, by research, to impact on both our health and energy.

THE CHALLENGE

If you ask someone the top three things that are bothering them, chances are, one of them will be people related. If you ask a business owner to list the top three things that keep them awake at night, chances are one will be people related. The fact is, for most people, their relationships bring them pain as well as joy.

THE SOLUTION

The great news is it doesn't have to be this way. In this section, I cover some of the simple-yet-important habits that will allow you not only to achieve more positive, quality relationships with the people in your life, but to attract more great people along the way.

Put yourself first

Remember, the most important person in your life is you. If you treat yourself with love, you will automatically improve the quality of all the relationships in your life. We all radiate a certain energy, so by being aware of our own energy, and ensuring it is a positive energy, we will attract more great people into our lives whose positive energy resonates with our energy.

Accept your differences

If we accept that we are all different, we can avoid a lot of pain and problems when dealing with others. All too often, we expect people to think, talk and act as we would in a situation, and then when they don't, we become frustrated.

If you really appreciate someone's differences in any situation, you create understanding instead of frustration and thereby improve the quality of your interactions with people who are different to you.

Give your full attention

There is nothing more effective in increasing the quality of the relationships in your life than giving whomever you are with your full attention. As covered in the section 'turn off your phone', you cannot give your full attention to someone while you continually check your messages. In addition to turning off your phone, tune into the person you are with and really give them your full attention.

Listen intently

When you are with someone, focusing your awareness on listening to that person dramatically improves the quality of your connection with him or her. This involves not taking things personally. When you are fully in the moment you will sometimes hear things to which you might usually react. Just listen and recognise that it is rarely personal, so there is no need to judge.

Make honesty your habit

Honesty can be a habit that many find challenging. However, as with all habits, with practice, it becomes natural, even easy. Honesty can be kind but it can also be hurtful if not presented with kindness. Practise honesty in all the relationships in your life, and if you feel your honesty could bring about hurt, do your best to be kind with your honesty. This simple habit can transform your relationships, while being tremendously freeing for yourself.

Avoid trying to change others

A common habit is that of trying to change other people, either because you are frustrated with what you see in another person or because you genuinely want to help them. However, accepting a person as he or she is in this moment is not only an act of love to the person but an act of love to yourself. All you need to focus on is being in this moment with each person and accepting them fully as they are right now.

Avoid assumptions

Refraining from making assumptions makes the relationships in your life less effortful. All too often, we think, speak and act with people on the basis of assumptions, and more often than not, our assumptions are wrong. Instead, cultivate the habit of asking questions. This simple habit will allow you to find the truth of a situation and most people will value being asked about things, rather than having you make assumptions.

Show compassion

While much of each individual's health, energy and happiness is within their own control, people find themselves in tough situations. I believe that if we could all show more compassion and understanding towards others, it really would make a big difference to the way we live. Try consistently practising compassion to others for a month and see the difference it makes to your life and to those around you.

Be kind with your words and actions

Kindness works in close partnership with compassion. Be kinder with your words and actions towards others. Research in the area of positive psychology shows this small habit has a big impact on your own happiness as well as that of others.

SUMMARY

As with all the habits in this book, your people habits need focus and an investment of time. However, not only will you see your relationships improve over time as you practise these habits, you will also enjoy some instant results. Use this instant positive feedback to motivate you to keep working on these people habits and see how your health, energy and happiness improves.

EVERYDAY HABITS TO CREATE MORE HAPPINESS AND SUCCESS

INTRODUCTION

As already outlined, the essence of mindfulness is doing one thing at a time with all your focus.

Let this be your mantra to transform your life.

THE CHALLENGE

We often rush through the small tasks in life as if they are obstacles to be dealt with quickly, before we move on to the next big thing. During these times, we miss the beauty of life and this becomes a habit.

THE SOLUTION

If you apply the mantra of doing one thing at a time with all your focus to the small, everyday tasks, you can bring more joy, gratitude and energy to each event which, in turn, flows into all the areas of your life.

As well as urging you to do one thing at a time with all your focus, I have also given you a few pointers that will help you to bring your attention fully to the task in hand.

You may read some of these and think they all sound a bit basic and boring. But imagine, if this were your last 10 minutes on the planet and you happened to be doing one of these simple daily activities. How would you do it?

The more often you practise doing one thing at a time, with all your focus, the more this will become your natural way. This also means you will move away from being constantly distracted by technology or thinking about the past or future.

Talk positively

At times, it can be hard to change how you feel. It can also be hard to control the thoughts that flow through your mind. However, one thing over which we all have control is the words we use. Creating a habit of being mindful and aware of the words we use is a powerful habit for health, happiness, relationships and success. Be impeccable with your words so that you only speak positively about yourself and others. This also applies to your own internal dialogue.

Be 'in the moment' in the shower

Having a morning shower gives you a great opportunity to start your day by doing one thing at a time, with a focus on your senses. I often find that if I am fully in the moment with all my senses when showering, this carries on to the next activity such as brushing my teeth or getting dressed.

Be aware while walking

It's common to see people walking along the street either lost in their thoughts or on their phones, missing the beauty that surrounds them. Create the habit of being fully aware in this moment next time you walk. Really focus on the beauty that surrounds you and you may just see something or someone magical.

Practise yoga with your full focus

Yoga can be a great way to do one thing at a time by fully focusing on your breath and the muscles you are stretching. Next time you do a yoga class, or yoga at home, make this focus your intention before you start and see how your yoga experience changes.

Spend more quality time with your hobbies

This can often be an area of your life in which mindfulness happens effortlessly. When you have a hobby you really love, you may become totally lost in the moment and time flies by. You have no interest in your phone or your thoughts and every part of you is in this moment.

So what is your hobby? And if you don't have one, what could it be? Running, reading, playing a musical instrument, cooking – the list is endless. I have three very simple suggestions for you:

1. If you have a hobby you love, prioritise it and spend as much time as possible on this hobby.

2. Really remember the feeling this hobby generates and aim to bring that same feeling of being fully in the moment into other areas of your life.

3. If you haven't yet identified your hobby, keep searching until you find one you love, that energises you and allows you to become present in the moment.

Have a Matcha tea ritual

Matcha tea has its origins in Japan. Japanese monks are famous for their Matcha tea ritual prior to meditation. Not only does Matcha tea taste great, but it also has many benefits for your energy, focus and overall health. So try Matcha tea, and when you do, really take time to drink it and fully appreciate it as if you were a Japanese monk.

Enjoy tidying

As described in the evening habit, 'prepare for sleep', a great time during which to tidy your home is your last hour before bed, once you've turned off all the technology.

This last hour can really help to calm the mind ready for sleep by bringing all your focus to tidying your home. Equally, the opposite is true – if you spend your last hour tidying while thinking continuously, you will go to bed with your mind racing. Use this last hour to calm the mind by doing one thing at a time, with all your focus.

Take pleasure in food shopping

One important way to ensure you have a healthy diet is to be aware of the food you buy. When you go shopping, really enjoy the process and commit to choosing nutritionally rich foods and drinks that benefit your body and reduce or avoid buying nutritionally poor, processed foods. Shopping for healthy food is made easier if you avoid shopping when you are hungry.

Be the best you can be

Always do your best in this moment. This simple habit will help you to achieve greater health, energy and happiness. If you can always say with pride that you did your best in this moment, you cannot ask for anything more. This will also mean you can stop comparing yourself to others, which is never a good move. Instead, compare yourself to you at your best – what you are capable of achieving.

Once this becomes your habit and natural way, you will see your health, energy and happiness improve. The other great thing about this habit is that your best will evolve and keep getting better.

Finally, remember each moment is a new moment, so if you ever feel you have not been very mindful throughout the day and have resorted to bad habits, the very fact that you have recognised this means that you are being mindful – and therefore, with this recognition and the new moment, you can begin practising again. Without judgement, be kind and compassionate to yourself as you begin again.

SUMMARY

Use these everyday activities to do one thing at a time with all your focus. Become fully aware of your senses during these activities. The more you practise doing one thing at a time, with all your focus, the easier this will become and the more you will find this is your natural way.

Most importantly, the more you practise this, the greater the number of amazing benefits you will experience from living in this way.

MY TOP 10 CORE HABITS

Inside this book, there are more than 100 positive habits. Further to this, when you dive into each habit you will find there are many more, for example, in the 'minimise' habit in the nutrition section; you may create a new habit of eating red meat just once a month, or drinking coffee every other morning. This means there are literally hundreds of habit variations inside this book. The habits you introduce will be personal to you.

Over time, you will start to create what I call your core habits. These are habits that you have grown to love, both for how you feel while you experience them and for the great benefits that come from consistently practising them.

Your core habits become your foundation for excellent health, energy and happiness.

As an example, I have listed 10 of my core habits and the reasons I love them. Your top 10 will be personal to you, and you will only create your top 10 by making three new habit changes per month.

Finally, remember the 80/20 rule. As long as you practise your core habits 80% of the time or more, you will benefit, so no need for perfection.

1. I DO ONE THING AT A TIME WITH ALL MY FOCUS

This is the essence of mindfulness. It allows me to enjoy life to the fullest and it plays a key role in my creativity and performance, both in work and in my free time.

2. I HAVE MY EVENING MEAL AT ABOUT 6PM

This is made up of a high-protein food and lots of vegetables. Eating early gives my body around four hours to digest my food before I go to bed. This improves my sleep and boosts my energy the next day. The protein food and the vitamins and minerals in the vegetables are helping my body to repair and recover overnight.

3. I AVOID ALL TECHNOLOGY FOR AN HOUR BEFORE BED

This helps me to calm my nervous system from all the stimulation of the day and improves my sleep. This, in turn, has a positive effect on my energy the following day.

4. MOST NIGHTS, I'M IN BED BY 10PM

This helps me to achieve a great night's sleep. Research shows that the hours between 10pm and 2am are often hours of high-quality sleep. This boosts my energy the next day, while also helping to ensure I wake early, giving me time for my morning habits.

5. I PRACTISE 20 MINUTES OF TM MEDITATION AS SOON AS I WAKE UP

This truly is the most beautiful way to start a day. My mind feels happy, sharp and creative and the positive feelings I have while I meditate help to ensure my day is a positive one.

6. I EXERCISE FOR 20-90 MINUTES EVERY MORNING

After spending eight hours sleeping, and then a further 20 minutes in meditation, and with the knowledge that a big part of my day will be seated, my body wants to move. Each day, I vary the time, type and intensity of my exercise according to how my body and energy feels at the time. This habit helps to kick-start my energy for the day and, by exercising in the morning, I guarantee consistency.

7. I DRINK 1.5 LITRES OF WATER WITHIN APPROXIMATELY TWO HOURS OF WAKING

This habit hydrates me in the morning and helps my body to flush out toxins created overnight as a result of my body processing the food and drink from the day before. This also plays a key role in boosting my energy for the morning.

8. I EAT A HIGH-ENERGY BREAKFAST

I vary my breakfast, but generally I will combine a gluten-free, slow-release carbohydrate food such as buckwheat flakes, gluten-free oats or amaranth pops with seeds such as chia, shelled hemp or pumpkin seeds. I'll generally include a small amount of fruit and almond milk. This breakfast is nutritionally rich and will energise me for about three-to-four hours.

9. I WRITE DOWN MY THREE 'MUST DOS' FOR THE DAY

Taking the time to write down my three 'must do' actions for the day, is time well spent. Without a doubt, this simple habit plays a key role in my performance at work.

10. I TALK POSITIVELY

We all love to feel positive and happy. For me, the number one way to stay positive and happy is to always talk positively. You may have times when your thoughts and feelings are not positive, but you always have control over your words. As with all the habits in this book, it takes practice at first, then it becomes effortless and natural.

Twenty tips and quotes to inspire you to do **one thing at a time** with all your focus:

"Mindfulness, paying
attention to the present
moment with your full intent"
(anon)

"Do every act of your
life, like it's the last
act of your life"
(anon)

"Mindfulness isn't
difficult; we just need to
remember to do it"
(anon)

"Do not dwell in the past,
do not dream of the future,
concentrate your mind on the
present moment"

(Buddha)

"In today's rush, we all think
too much, seek too much,
want too much and forget
about the joy of just being"

(Eckhart Tolle)

"The best way to capture
moments is to pay attention.
This is how we cultivate
mindfulness"

(anon)

"Mindfulness means being awake. It means knowing what you are doing"

(Jon Kabat-Zinn)

"Feelings come and go like clouds in a windy sky. Conscious breathing is my anchor"

(Thich Nhat Hanh)

"As long as you are breathing there is more right with you, than wrong with you"

(anon)

"Don't just look, observe.
Don't just swallow, taste.

Don't just think, feel.
Don't just exist, live"

(anon)

"It's only when we truly know
and understand that we
have a limited time on earth
and that we have no way of
knowing when our time is up,
we will begin to live each day
to the fullest, as if it was the
only one we had"

(Elisabeth Kübler-Ross)

"Each morning we are born again. What we do today is what matters most"

(Buddha)

"Be happy in the moment, that's enough. Each moment is all we need, not more"

(Mother Teresa)

"Whatever the present moment contains, accept it as if you had chosen it. Always work with it, not against it"

(Eckhart Tolle)

"We're so busy watching out for what's just ahead of us that we don't take time to enjoy where we are"

(Bill Watterson)

"There is only one time that is important – now!"

(anon)

"When you are here and now, sitting totally, not jumping ahead, the miracle has happened. To be in the moment is the miracle"

(Osho)

"Life is available only in the present moment. If you abandon the present moment you cannot live the moments of your daily life deeply"

(Thich Nhat Hanh)

"The secret of health for both mind and body is not to mourn for the past, worry about the future, or anticipate troubles, but to live in the present moment wisely and earnestly"

(Buddha)

"Don't let yesterday use
up too much of today"

(Cherokee Indian proverb)

"The past is a ghost, the
future a dream. All we ever
have is now"

(anon)

Twenty tips and quotes to **inspire you** with your habit changes:

"Change your habits.
Change your life"

(Oliver Gray)

"Motivation is what gets
you started; habit is what
keeps you going"

(anon)

"Good habits are worth
being fanatical about"

(anon)

"Success is the sum of small efforts, repeated day in and day out"

(anon)

"No one can change your habits for you, you have to be the one that makes it happen"

(anon)

"Start with a habit change so easy you can't say no to it"

(anon)

"A year from now you'll wish you started that morning exercise habit"

(anon)

"How long do you want
to continue to live your
bad habits?"

(anon)

"There is no better time
to change a bad habit
than today"

(anon)

"If you change nothing,
nothing will change"

(anon)

"Good habits are as addictive
as bad habits but much
more rewarding"

(anon)

"Three habits that will energise your day: go to bed early, meditate, and exercise each morning"

(Oliver Gray)

"Willpower and focus are muscles, the more you use them the stronger they get"

(anon)

"It takes 30 days of focus to make or break a habit"

(Oliver Gray)

"One beautiful gift we have as humans is choice, so choose your habits wisely"

(anon)

"Once you see the results from your daily exercise habit, it becomes addictive"

(anon)

"Results come through daily practice not extra knowledge"

(anon)

"Seek small improvements one day at a time, then eventually you have a big improvement"

(anon)

"There's no elevator to health, energy and happiness. You have to take the stairs"

(anon)

"To begin. Begin".

(anon)

FINAL WORDS

Thank you for reading.

Do one thing at a time with all your focus and be mindful of the decisions you make.

Dedicate yourself to mastering this and you are a mindfulness master.

Remember, knowledge is only 1% of the deal and extra knowledge won't change your life.

Focus on a maximum of three habit changes at any one time.

Practise… Practise… Practise!

When your habits change, your life changes.

I really enjoyed writing this book, I hope you enjoy making your changes.

I wish you health, energy and happiness

Oliver

PS: if you have any questions about the content in this book, or would like to send me your feedback or any success stories, I'd love to hear from you. You can reach me via email at Oliver@energiseyou.com

READING LIST

MEDITATION AND RELAXATION

For more information on (TM) Transcendental Meditation visit
www.energiseyou.com/tm-meditation

For a great selection of alpha music visit
www.silenceofmusic.com/shop/

For some guided meditation download one of the many guided meditation apps such as headspace.

For a demonstration of the semi-supine Alexander technique position visit youtube. The Alexander technique teaches you to use your body in a more natural effortless way and helps to improve your posture.

DISCOVERING YOUR STRENGTHS

A great book to help you to discover your strengths is *Strengthsfinder 2.0* by Tom Rath. This book comes with access to a great online test to help you discover your natural strengths.

NUTRITION

For an excellent food intolerance test I'd recommend
www.yorktest.com

ABOUT THE AUTHOR

Oliver Gray is an ex-professional tennis player and personal trainer. He went on to manage 14 central London health clubs and qualified as a neuro-linguistic programming (NLP) practitioner before founding EnergiseYou in 2004, the UK's first health and energy corporate coaching business.

Since 2004, EnergiseYou has energised in excess of 40,000 employees in more than 500 organisations, achieving a 98% satisfaction score from the employees they have coached.

Oliver is author of the book *EnergiseYou, The Ultimate Health and Energy Plan*. His second book, *Feel Great,* is based on 20 years' experience in the area of health, energy and happiness.